Conduit Bending Workbook
By Tom Henry

National Electrical Code® and NEC® are Registered Trademarks of the National Fire Protection Association, Inc., Quincy, MA.

Fourth printing January 2003   **ISBN 0 - 945495 - 57 - 9**

ENRY PUBLICATIONS SINCE 1985

Preface

I have designed this conduit bending training program on bending conduit with a *hand bender* which is used up to 1 1/4" EMT.

The student needs to learn how to make the bends that are made on the job. You learn conduit bending by doing it!

This program with the video and the workbook will teach not only where to place the pencil mark on the conduit, but also the important elements such as: Which direction do you make bend, away from or towards the last fitting?

You will learn how to make the correct bends when going towards an obstruction so there is no adjusting the conduit after the bend is made by cutting the conduit, adding couplings, nipples, etc.

I find many books that show a mark on the conduit and you measure from that mark and make your first bend. What does the first mark represent? In our training program you will learn that the first mark is from the last coupling or box and we are calculating our bend from that point. So you won't be cutting conduit to make it fit, wasting material and labor hours. We'll learn how to allow for the shrinkage amount and calculate it into our bend and bend it right the first time!

It's easy to learn, if you see the picture. This workbook is filled with pictures showing you the position of the hands, feet, bender head, direction of bend, conduit on floor, conduit in the air, foot pressure, hand pressure, etc.

This conduit training program is the true example of " a picture is worth a thousand words".

Forget the algebra and all the words that some can't even spell and I'll train you with pictures is the way I have designed this program.

You will need a 1/2" EMT bender head (approximately $15 to $20) and handle (you can make your own from a 38" (965mm piece of 3/4" IMC) and five or six 10' lengths of 1/2" EMT to practice the examples in this workbook.

Again, you learn by *doing*!

Conduit bending or it may be more proper to call it the curving of a tubing. The most popular raceway is the electrical metallic *tubing*, better known as thin-wall or EMT.

To make a bend is to turn or force from straight to curved or angular. If conduit is bent at a sharp angle to where the conduit is kinked it then makes the pulling of the wires more difficult.

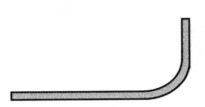

To curve is to have or take a turn, change, or deviation from a straight line without sharps breaks or angularity.

The quality of one's work can not always be judged as it may be covered by walls, ceilings, etc. but *exposed* conduit work is there for all to see.

You don't have to be a rocket scientist or trigonometric major to bend conduit.

The only way you will actually learn how to bend conduit is by actually doing it. Actual experience soon makes this operation simple and routine.

The student will not realize the full value of the information unless he reinforces his study with a reasonable amount of practical work.

TO M$_S$ TiPS

Code section 110-12 states electrical equipment shall be installed in a neat workmanlike manner.

WHY INSTALL CONDUIT?

Conduit provides mechanical protection to protect conductors, permits easy wiring modifications.

WHY BEND CONDUIT? Conduit fittings such as sweeping el's, factory elbows, boxes, or condulet fittings such as LB's, LL's, and LR's can be used to make almost any bend.

Conduit bending saves money as it is faster, more economical, and saves cutting and reaming time.

The fewer number of conduit fittings used in the raceway system the more effective the grounding path will be if you're using the metal conduit as the grounding conductor.

Condulet fittings such as LL's, LR's, and LB's are used mostly to turn corners.

TYPES OF HAND BENDERS

Hickey and roll-type hand bender. There are also mechanical benders and hydraulic benders for the larger size conduits.

The roll-type hand bender is most commonly used on EMT with sizes 1/2" (13mm), 3/4" (19mm), 1" (25mm) and 1 1/4" (32mm). It is the most common hand bender. They have high supporting sidewalls to prevent flattening or kinking of the tubing and a long arc that permits the making of 90° bends in a single sweep without having to move the bender to a new position along the tubing as you would with a hickey type hand bender.

Don't confuse the hickey with the roll-type hand bender. Both are used to bend conduit by hand, but in totally different ways. The roll-type bender supports the walls of the conduit and provides a bending radius that conforms to the Code requirements.

The hickey is used for rigid conduit only and the person holding the handle must form the bend as well as the radius as the bender is applied. This must be done in such a manner so as not to flatten or kink the conduit. The hickey is used somewhat like the hydraulic bender as you make segment bends. Several segment 10° bends are made to complete the bend at the proper radius. Hickeys should not be used to bend EMT because very little support is given to the walls of the conduit.

Less skill is required in using a roll-type bender compared to a hickey-type.

Bending rigid conduit is a laborious and time consuming process. Thinwall conduit has replaced rigid conduit in many installations because it's easier to bend and can be installed quicker.

Rigid is used generally for mechanical protection or in hazardous locations. Where the conduit is exposed to mechanical damage rigid is the choice. In the walls and ceilings where the conduit is concealed, generally thinwall is used.

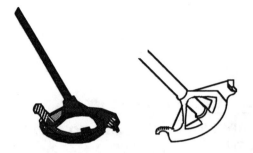

Several manufacturer's make conduit benders. Read the instructions that came with the bender.

Roll-type hand benders are available in sizes 1/2" (13mm) to 1 1/4" (32mm). Electrical metallic conduit, also referred to as "EMT" or thinwall is bent with hand benders up to 1" (25mm) in size, and 1 1/4" for small offsets. Larger sizes are bent with hydraulic benders. Small sizes of rigid steel, intermediate metal conduit (IMC), and aluminum conduit use this same bender. A 3/4" EMT roll-type bender will also bend 1/2" rigid.

THINWALL	RIGID
3/4"	1/2"
1"	3/4"
1 1/4"	1"

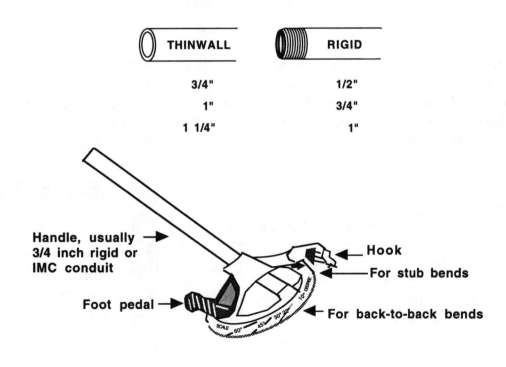

Handle, usually 3/4 inch rigid or IMC conduit

Foot pedal

Hook

For stub bends

For back-to-back bends

TH
3

Manufacturers cast bold symbols, arrows, stars, etc., on the bending shoe to mark the center of the bend and degree scales (slash marks) on the sides of the bender to mark the degrees of bend for accuracy. These cast markings are usually recessed and filled with paint for easy identification. The radius of the bending shoe of the bender is based on the minimum radius for each size of conduit in the National Electrical Code. The hook area at the front of the bender has a ribbed interior to grip the conduit and prevent the conduit from slipping. This ribbed interior is designed so as to not knick or score the conduit. The back end of the bender has a non-skid foot pedal for constant foot pressure during the bend and increases leverage by 75 percent. The top of the bender has recessed threads for the handle to be installed.

SLASH MARKS TO INDICATE DEGREE OF BEND

•It's very important to understand the symbol markings on the bender you are using.

BENDER SYMBOLS ON DIFFERENT BENDER HEADS		
90° STUB-UP	**3-POINT SADDLE CENTER BEND**	**BACK TO BACK BEND MARK**
ARROW	TEAR DROP	STAR
	RIM NOTCHES ON BOTTOM OF SHOE	"B" MARK
	"A" MARK	

Hand benders are shipped without handles. A handle is often made in the field by cutting and threading a piece of *rigid* steel conduit or IMC. It's best to buy a bender handle manufactured by the bender company. These bender handles will not bend, they stay straight, and the threads are tapered so that the handle tightens firmly into the bender. A bender with a crooked handle is awkward to work with. The length of the handle is important. It gives proper leverage for bending and the proper length also provides better body balance when working with the bender.

SUGGESTED HANDLE LENGTHS		
1/2" bender	38 inches	*965mm*
3/4" bender	38 inches	*965mm*
1" bender	44 inches	*1.12m*
1 1/4" bender	54 inches	*1.37m*

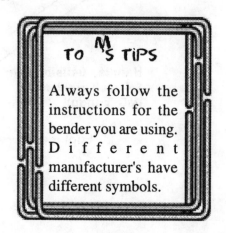

TOM'S TIPS

Always follow the instructions for the bender you are using. Different manufacturer's have different symbols.

90° Stub Bend The 90° stub bend is probably the most basic and the most bent. All other bends are less than 90°. Let's practice bending a stub-up.

Take a 10' (3.05m) length of 1/2" EMT and cut it in half and lay one piece on the floor. For a 12 inch (305mm) 90° stub up, take a rule and measure 7 inches (178mm) from the end of the conduit and with a pencil make a mark completely around the conduit. The 7" (178mm) mark is the 12" (305mm) minus the take up 5" (127mm).

Take your 1/2" EMT bender in your hand and with your other hand, lift the conduit off the floor just enough to place the conduit into the hook of the bender and place the pencil mark on the conduit on the arrow mark on the bender.

With the conduit firmly on the floor put your right foot on the conduit and your left foot on the foot pedal at the back of the bender. Bend the conduit straight up just past the 90° mark on your bender (this allows for a small amount of kick back) keeping constant pressure on the foot pedal.

In general bender take-ups (the length that must be subtracted from the desired stub length) are:

BENDER TAKE-UP TABLE		
1/2" E.M.T.	5"	(127mm)
3/4" E.M.T. - 1/2" Rigid	6"	(152mm)
1" E.M.T. - 3/4" Rigid	8"	(203mm)
1 1/4" E.M.T. - 1" Rigid	11"	(279mm)

The take-up is the distance measured from the arrow or reference point on the bender to the back side of the conduit after the 90° bend is made.

Use a wide stance, feet 30" (762mm) apart. If right handed put heavy pressure on left foot on the bender. Keep right foot on the conduit.

TO M'S TiPS

The stronger the foot pressure the more accurate the bend.

All 90° bends should be made on a **hard surface** floor (not carpet). Bending conduit on carpet may cause flattening of the bend.

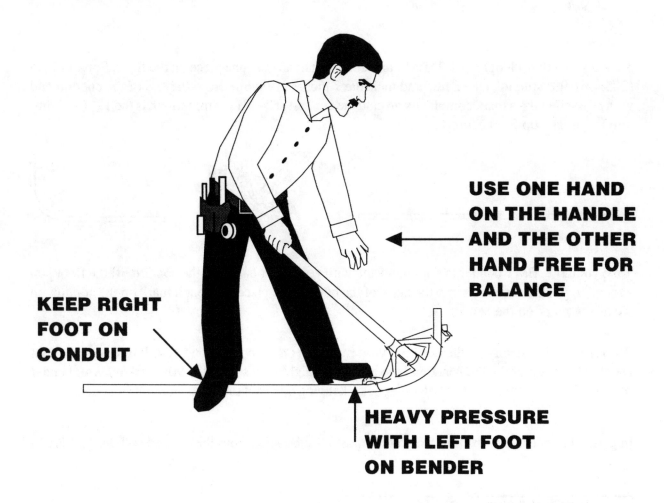

USE ONE HAND ON THE HANDLE AND THE OTHER HAND FREE FOR BALANCE

KEEP RIGHT FOOT ON CONDUIT

HEAVY PRESSURE WITH LEFT FOOT ON BENDER

Remember to keep constant **foot pressure** throughout the full bend for the most accurate bend.

38" (965mm) is the best length for a handle on a 1/2" or 3/4" bender. A longer handle encourages too much pull on the it. Remember, **foot pressure** is accuracy, not handle pull. Conduit is curved into a gradual sweep to avoid flattening.

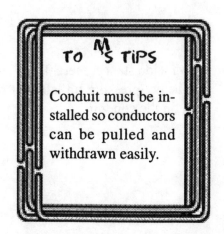

TO M'S TIPS

Conduit must be installed so conductors can be pulled and withdrawn easily.

RADIUS OF THE BEND

It is the radius of the angle formed by the shoe of the bender that has to be considered. Different shoe units for different size conduit benders are purposely constructed with different diameters and radii.

If the radius is too small you would have trouble pulling the wire around the 90° bend than you would a 90° bend with a larger radius.

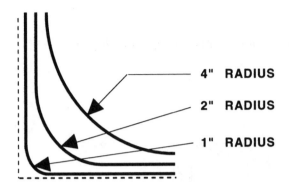

4" RADIUS

2" RADIUS

1" RADIUS

The larger 4" (102mm) radius will allow the wires to be pulled easier through the conduit. Also, the larger the radius, the greater the length of conduit gain will be.

With a shoe unit on a bender you can make the bend in one continuous curve or motion of the bender.

With a shoe unit, the required bend is easy to make, but with a *hickey bender* you have to be careful to obey the radius requirements. Several small segment bends are required to make a 90° bend with a hickey.

The roll-type bender provides a bending radius that conforms to the Code requirements.

STANDARD CONDUIT BENDS	
TRADE SIZE	MINIMUM RADIUS TO CENTER OF CONDUIT
1/2" (13mm)	4" (102mm)
3/4" (19mm)	4 1/2" (114mm)
1" (25mm)	5 3/4" (146mm)

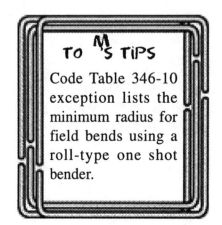

TOM'S TIPS

Code Table 346-10 exception lists the minimum radius for field bends using a roll-type one shot bender.

BACK TO BACK BENDS

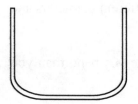

A back to back bend is two 90° bends spaced a distance apart in the conduit forming a "U" shape.

After the first 90° bend has been made (A), measure to the point where the **back** of the second 90° bend is to be made (B).

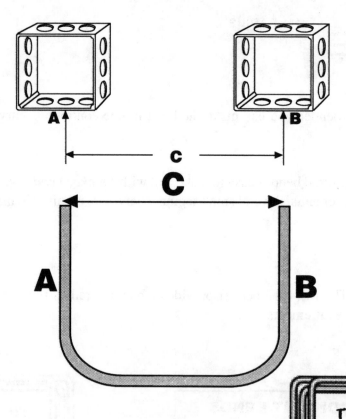

Benders have a mark, line, star, or symbols on the bender head to indicate where to place your pencil mark for the back on the second 90° bend.

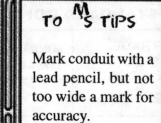

TO **M**S TIPS

Mark conduit with a lead pencil, but not too wide a mark for accuracy.

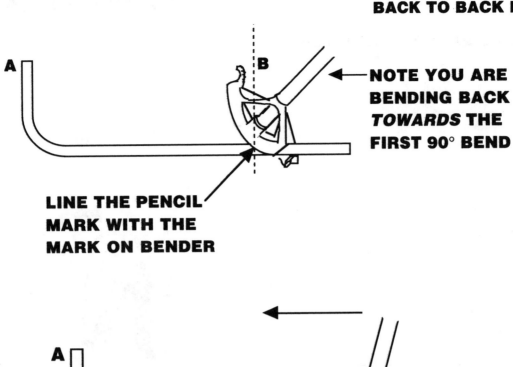

NOTE YOU ARE BENDING BACK *TOWARDS* THE FIRST 90° BEND

LINE THE PENCIL MARK WITH THE MARK ON BENDER

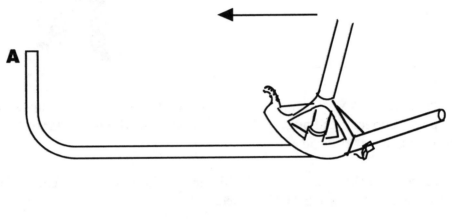

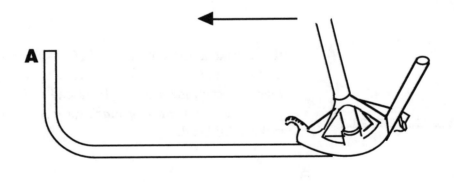

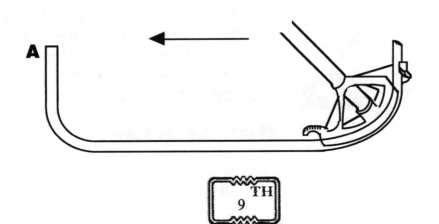

PRACTICE BACK TO BACK BENDS

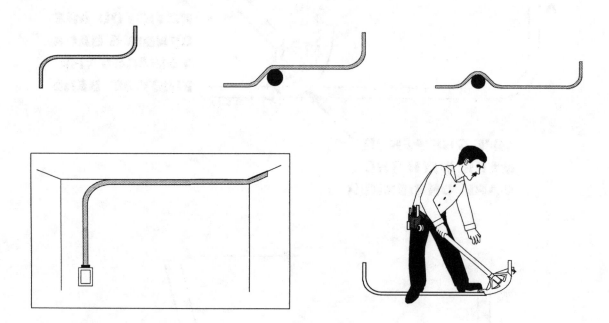

The back to back bend is a very common bend made on the job site. It's a matter of measuring between two points correctly and placing the second pencil mark on the star or "B" mark on the bender head and making a 90° bend.

To practice, take a 10' (305m) length of 1/2" EMT and cut into two pieces each 5 feet (1.52m) in length. Practice bending with one 5' (1.52m) piece.

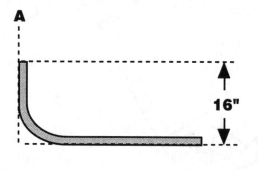

•First make a 90° stub bend of 16" (406mm) in height. Deduct 5" (127mm) for take up. 16" - 5" = 11" (279mm). Make a pencil mark at 11" from end of conduit. Place pencil mark on the ***arrow mark*** for stub up bends. Now make a 90° bend.

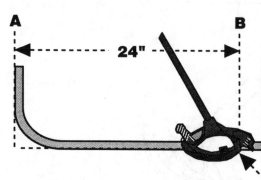

•Use 24" (610mm) for the distance between the back to back bends. Make a pencil mark at 24" on the conduit from point "A". Place the pencil mark on the marking on bender head for back of bend (star or "B" mark). Remember to pull bender towards point "A".

MAKE PENCIL MARK

TH
10

Now measure between "A" and "B" to see how close to 24" you are. You should have approximately 25 1/4" (641mm) in height at stub-up "B".

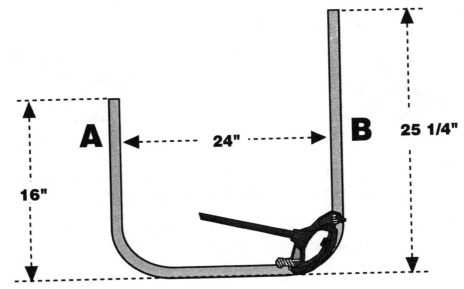

If the back to back bends are *too close together*, then reverse the bender and make a stub-up bend. Now deduct 5" (127mm) for 1/2" EMT and put your pencil mark on the *arrow* for a stub-up bend.

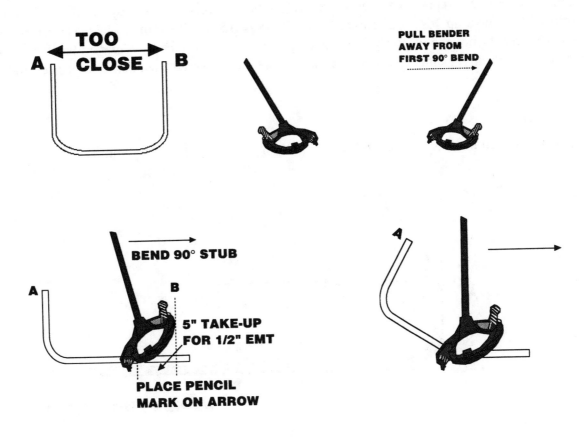

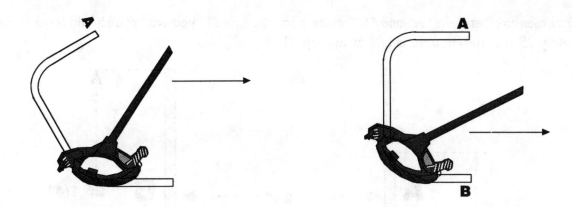

If distance "C" is too *long*, install the bender to the same pencil mark and *overbend* the 90° to 115° or 120°. Then push the bend back to 90°. This will shorten distance "C".

If distance "C" is too *short*, straighten the conduit and re-bend it to a shorter radius using a *hickey type* bender. •*This will be explained later in more detail.*

In the next example we'll bend a back to back that is *close together*.

Take the other 5' (1.52m) piece and start by bending a 20 1/2" (521mm) stub-up of 90°. Deduct 5" (127mm) for the take-up for a 1/2" conduit. 20 1/2" - 5" = 15 1/2 (394mm)". Make a pencil mark 15 1/2" (394mm) from end of conduit and place pencil mark at the *arrow mark* on bender. Now make the 90° stub-up remembering to keep constant foot pressure on the bender for accurate bends.

Next make a pencil mark on the conduit for the back of point "B" at 24" (610mm).

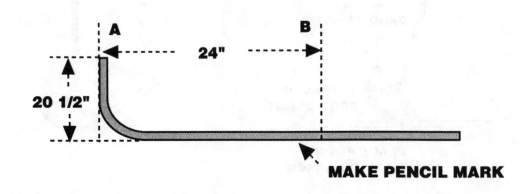

MAKE PENCIL MARK

Now deduct 5" (127mm) from the 24" mark and make a pencil mark and line this pencil mark up with the *arrow mark* on the bender. Now reverse the direction of the bender so you will be bending *away* from point "A" instead of having your back to point "A" you'll be facing point "A" as you make the second 90° stub bend. Make sure your first stub-up bend is straight up as you start your second bend.

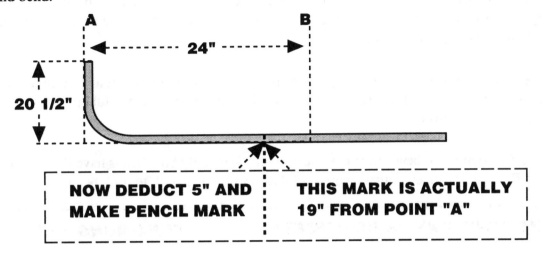

A   B

24"

20 1/2"

NOW DEDUCT 5" AND MAKE PENCIL MARK   **THIS MARK IS ACTUALLY 19" FROM POINT "A"**

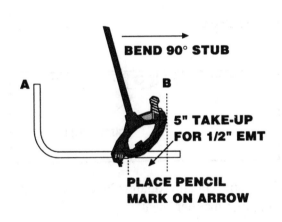

BEND 90° STUB

A   B

5" TAKE-UP FOR 1/2" EMT

PLACE PENCIL MARK ON ARROW

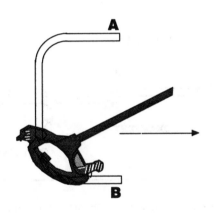

A

B

Measure for the 24" (127mm) between "A" and "B". You should have two stub-ups approximately 20 1/2" (521mm) each.

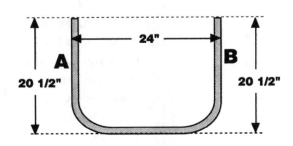

24"

A   B

20 1/2"   20 1/2"

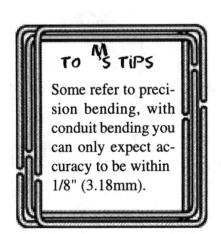

TO **M**S TiPS

Some refer to precision bending, with conduit bending you can only expect accuracy to be within 1/8" (3.18mm).

OFFSET BENDS

The purpose of the offset is to allow the conduit to enter fittings, fixtures, boxes, etc. without placing any strain on the boxes, etc., into which the conduit enters or on the conduit clamps. The offset should be parallel to the conduit.

An offset is a bend that takes the tubing out of line with the run but then returns it in a direction parallel to the original run. It is two separate bends. The first bend takes the tubing out of line, and the second bend returns it.

An offset is actually two bends in opposite directions. Generally both bends have the same degree of bend. Bending an offset requires more skill than a stub-up or back to back bend.

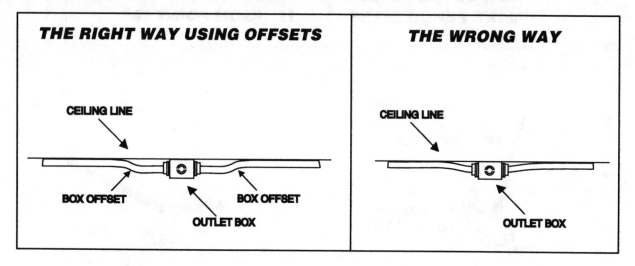

Conduit should not be run on a slant, conduit work should be straight and square. Code section 110-12 requires electrical installations to be done in a workmanlike manner (neat).

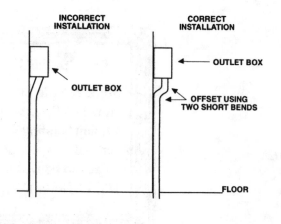

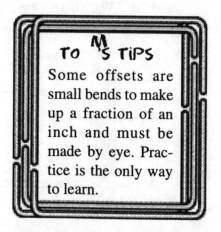

TO M'S TIPS
Some offsets are small bends to make up a fraction of an inch and must be made by eye. Practice is the only way to learn.

Conduit bending saves money as it is faster, more economical, and saves cutting and reaming time.

The box to the left is required to be clamped within 3' (914mm) of the box.
The conduit must be offset to the wall by bending an offset or by installing a factory made offset fitting.

FACTORY OFFSET

A pipe clamp as shown could be used and would secure the conduit to the Code requirements.

The fewer number of conduit fittings used in the raceway system the more effective the grounding path will be if you're using the metal conduit as the grounding conductor.

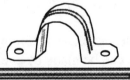

Condulet fittings such as LL's, LR's, and LB's are used mostly to turn corners.

TO M'S TIPS
The Code requires conduit to be securely fastened in place at least every 10' and within 3' of each box, conduit body, or other tubing termination.

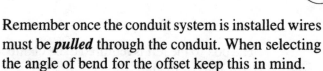

Remember once the conduit system is installed wires must be *pulled* through the conduit. When selecting the angle of bend for the offset keep this in mind.

The sharper the offset angle, the harder it will be to pull the wires through the conduit.

Bends shall be made so that the conduit will not be damaged and the internal diameter of the conduit will not be effectively reduced.

Kinks in the conduit can damage the wire insulation when the wire is pulled into the conduit.

A *30°* offset is one of the most efficient to pull through. The shallower the offset angle, the more space the bend will require.

When bending offsets you must consider the *shrinkage*. You will reduce the length of the conduit a certain amount for every degree of bend.

Remember, when you're *working toward* an obstruction, you'll have to *add* the shrinkage, but you'll ignore it when working away from the obstruction, unless you are calculating the *total length* of conduit.

Shallow offsets with depths of 3" (76mm) or 4" (102mm) are best with 30° bends maximum. More than 30° makes pulling the wire more difficult.

Offsets 5" (127mm) deep or more 45° bends are best. They take up less room and look neater.

For 2" (51mm) depths - 22 1/2° bends are best.

For little kicks 1" (25mm) or less into a box use 10° bends. After practice and experience small kicks can be made by eye.

Unlike the 90° stub-up bend that is measured over-all, the offset bend is measured bottom to bottom.

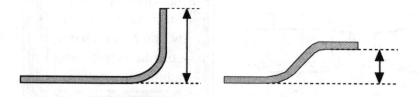

TO M S TIPS

Always bend conduit in an area that provides a level floor with secure footing and support.

The words "shrinkage" and "gain" are used in bending conduit.

When bending an offset going towards an object the length of conduit will *shrink* due to this *detour* and the object. The conduit will shorten.

It's like driving down a straight road to find it is closed due to a detour. The detour takes more road as it takes more conduit to make an offset. This is called the *shrinkage amount*.

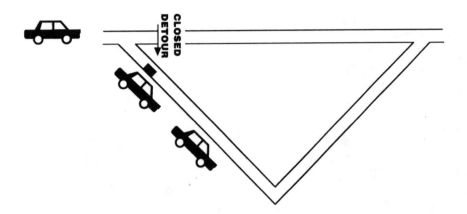

The only time we need to be concerned about the *gain* of a conduit is when installing *rigid* conduit and you want to *thread it before bending*. This is the only case where we will use the gain. It will be covered in more detail later in this workbook.

It takes less conduit to reach a point when it is curved rather than a sharp angle as shown above.

It's a shorter route to the same finish line as shown below. By sweeping the conduit in a radius we **gain** conduit compared to taking the long route.

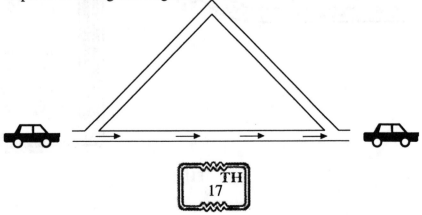

TH
17

UNDERSTANDING ANGLE OF DEGREES

A circle can be divided into four equal quadrants. Each quadrant accounts for 90° and makes a total of 360°. A quarter of a circle is one quadrant (90°).

When bending conduit we are within one quadrant (90°) or less.

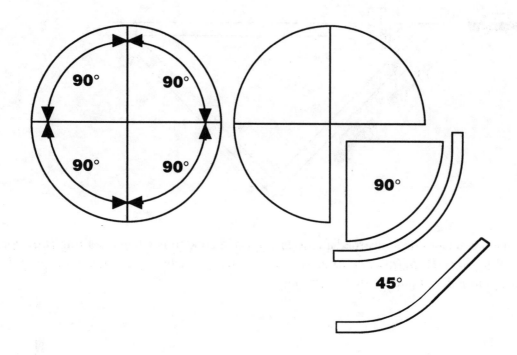

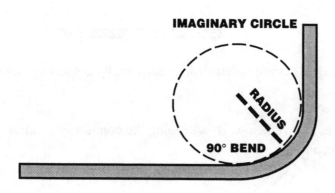

An overbend would be more than 90°. An overbend can be straightened.

You visualize the face of a clock. You bend from 6 PM to a maximum 3 PM (90°) counterclockwise.

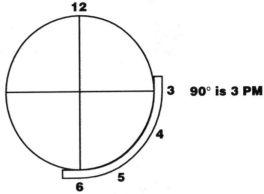

90° is 3 PM

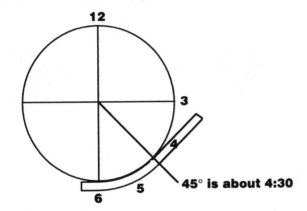

45° is about 4:30

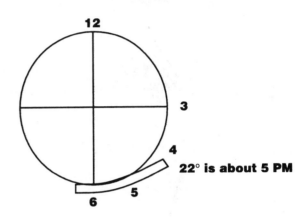

22° is about 5 PM

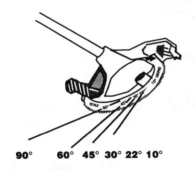

90°   60°   45°   30°   22°   10°

Most bender heads have markings showing the degree of bend. Some even have a built-in level to indicate 45° and 90°.

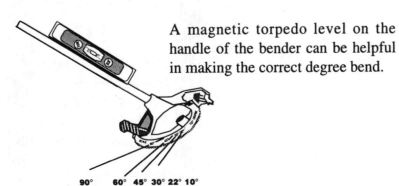

90°   60°   45°   30°   22°   10°

A magnetic torpedo level on the handle of the bender can be helpful in making the correct degree bend.

TO^MS TIPS

Keep in mind that shallow bends (22° & 30°) make for easier wire pulling. Steeper bends (45°) use less space.

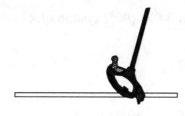

Different benders have different handle positions. With one style bender when the handle it *straight-up* you have bent a 30° angle. With another style bender you have bent a 45° angle with handle straight-up.

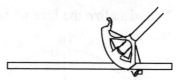

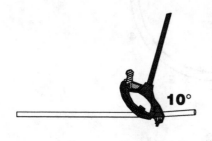

10°

22°

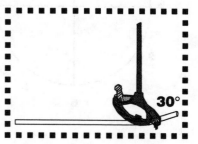

30°

10°

22°

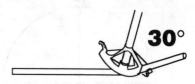

30°

45°

60°

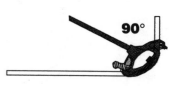

90°

45°

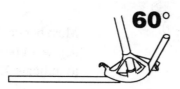

60°

90°

TO ^M~S~ TiPS

Never use a bender to bend *rebar* or any material other than EMT or rigid conduit of the size marked on the bender.

There are two ways to produce bends with a hand bender.

(1) With the conduit and bender on the floor with *heavy foot pressure*.

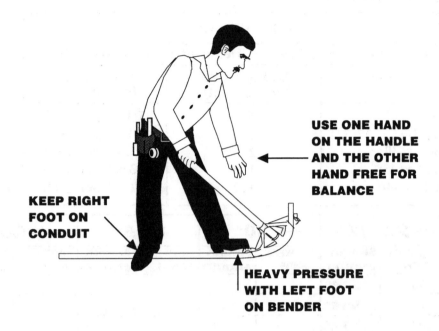

USE ONE HAND
ON THE HANDLE
AND THE OTHER
HAND FREE FOR
BALANCE

KEEP RIGHT
FOOT ON
CONDUIT

HEAVY PRESSURE
WITH LEFT FOOT
ON BENDER

(2) With the handle of the bender placed on the floor the conduit is bent off the floor with hand and
    arm pressure.

Keep the conduit under the armpit, hand
pressure close. As you bend the conduit
allow your body and the bender to lean
forward as you bend.

TO M'S TIPS

Guess work is slow
and sloppy. This
workbook will elimi-
nate the guess work.

Bends use some of the conduit length and an allowance must be made for this *shrinkage* between bends. If the offset is away from an obstruction, the shrink can be ignored. If you are making an offset into an area, the amount of shrinkage must be added to the measurement. The offset formula has been calculated into a chart shown below.

OFFSET FORMULA		
Distance between bends = Depth of offset x Multiplier		
Angle	Multiplier of Offset Depth	Shrinkage Per Inch of Rise
10° x 10°	6	1/16" per inch
22 1/2° x 22 1/2°	2.6	3/16" per inch
30° x 30°	2	1/4" per inch
45° x 45°	1.4	3/8" per inch
60° x 60°	1.2	1/2" per inch

DEGREE OF BEND →	22 1/2°		→ 30°		→ 45°		→ 60°	
OFFSET DEPTH	BETWEEN BENDS	SHRINK AMOUNT	BETWEEN BENDS	SHRINK AMOUNT	BETWEEN BENDS	SHRINK AMOUNT	BETWEEN BENDS	SHRINK AMOUNT
2"	5 1/4"	3/8"						
3"	7 3/4"	9/16"	6"	3/4"				
4"	10 1/2"	3/4"	8"	1"				
5"	13"	15/16"	10"	1 1/4"	7"	1 7/8"		
6"	15 1/2"	1 1/8"	12"	1 1/2"	8 1/2"	2 1/4"	7 1/4"	3"
7"	18 1/4"	1 5/16"	14"	1 3/4"	9 3/4"	2 5/8"	8 3/8"	3 1/2"
8"	20 3/4"	1 1/2"	16"	2"	11 1/4"	3"	9 5/8"	4"
9"	23 1/2"	1 3/4"	18"	2 1/4"	12 1/2"	3 3/8"	10 7/8"	4 1/2"
10"	26"	1 7/8"	20"	2 1/2"	14"	3 3/4"	12"	5"

The most commonly used angle is 30° for offsets. A multiplier of 2 is used for 30° bends which is easy multiplication and makes wire pulling easy. The smaller the angle of degree used for the offset, the easier the wire is to pull, but a large obstruction in the path of the conduit may require a 45° or larger angle to be used because the direction has to change in a small amount of space.

Offset depth x multiplier = the *distance between the bends*. When space is not a problem a smaller degree offset is more desirable.

For offsets 5 inches (127mm) or more use 45°.
For offsets of 3 (76mm) or 4 inches (102mm) use 30° bends.
For offsets of 2 inches (51mm) in depth use 22 1/2°.
For small offsets of 1 inch (25mm) or less use 10°.

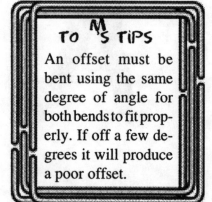

TO M'S TIPS
An offset must be bent using the same degree of angle for both bends to fit properly. If off a few degrees it will produce a poor offset.

When measuring to properly mark the conduit the student needs to understand the ruler markings which are in fractions. When using the charts we are required to multiply fractions and decimals.

Example: The angle of bend is 45° and the obstruction depth is 4 1/2" (114mm). What is the distance between bends?

The OFFSET FORMULA below shows a multiplier of 1.4. We would multiply the 4 1/2" (114mm) obstruction depth by 1.4. This is easy because most students know that 1/2" = .5. So 4.5" x 1.4 = 6.3". Now some ask where is 6.3" on the ruler which has 1/16" marks in fractions not decimals. Looking at the chart below .3 would be approximately 5/16". The distance between bends would be 6 5/16" (160mm).

OFFSET FORMULA		
Distance between bends = Depth of offset x Multiplier		
Angle	**Multiplier of Offset Depth**	**Shrinkage Per Inch**
10° x 10°	6	1/16" per inch
22 1/2° x 22 1/2°	2.6	3/16" per inch
30° x 30°	2	1/4" per inch
45° x 45°	1.4	3/8" per inch
60° x 60°	1.2	1/2" per inch

THIS RULER HAS 1/16" MARKINGS

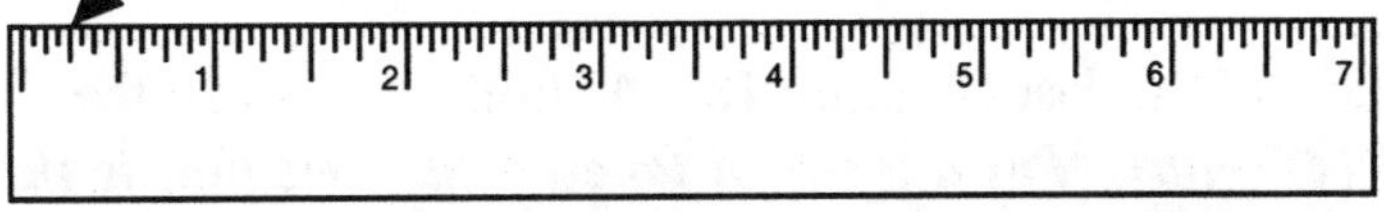

FRACTION OF INCH		DECIMAL	FRACTION OF INCH		DECIMAL
1/16"	(1.59mm)	.0625	9/16"	(14.29mm)	.5625
1/8"	(3.18mm)	.125	5/8"	(15.88mm)	.625
3/16"	(4.76mm)	.1875	11/16"	(17.46mm)	.6875
1/4"	(6.35mm)	.250	3/4"	(19.05mm)	.750
5/16"	(7.94mm)	.3125	13/16"	(20.64mm)	.8125
3/8"	(9.53mm)	.375	7/8"	(22.23mm)	.875
7/16"	(11.11mm)	.4375	15/16"	(23.81mm)	.9375
1/2"	(12.7mm)	.500	1"	(25.4mm)	1.0

Example: 15/16" = ?   Divide 15 by 16 in your calculator = 0.9375.

PRACTICE OFFSET BENDS

In the example below we have a 3 1/2" (89mm) obstruction that we need to bend a 30° offset in the conduit to lay on top of it. Since we are working *towards* the obstruction we need to calculate the shrinkage in the conduit due to the detour around the 3 1/2" (89mm) obstruction. Let's say the distance from the last coupling to the obstruction is 18" (457mm). Add the **SHRINK PER INCH** from the OFFSET FORMULA table.

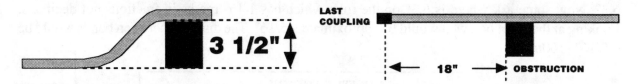

To practice, take a 10' (305m) length of 1/2" EMT and cut into two pieces each 5 feet (1.52m) in length. Bend the example with a 5' piece.

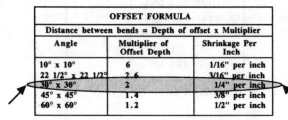

OFFSET FORMULA		
Distance between bends = Depth of offset x Multiplier		
Angle	Multiplier of Offset Depth	Shrinkage Per Inch
10° x 10°	6	1/16" per inch
22 1/2° x 22 1/2°	2.6	3/16" per inch
30° x 30°	2	1/4" per inch
45° x 45°	1.4	3/8" per inch
60° x 60°	1.2	1/2" per inch

The OFFSET FORMULA lists a "shrinkage per inch" of 1/4". Take the obstruction depth 3.5" x .250" = .875 or 7/8" (•Note: 7/8" (22mm) = .875)

Add 7/8" to the distance from last coupling 18" (457mm) and make the first pencil mark on the conduit at *18 7/8" (479mm).* •*Put a piece of tape on the end that is the last coupling, when bending this will always remind you which end is the last coupling end of conduit.*

To find the distance between the bends the OFFSET FORMULA shows using a muliplier of *2* for 30° bends. Multiply the offset depth 3.5" x 2 = 7". Make the second pencil mark at 7" (178mm) from the first mark.

PENCIL MARKS

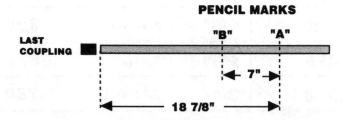

Align the first pencil mark "A" 18 7/8" (479mm) with stub-up *arrow* on bender. From the floor bend a 30° angle. Bending towards the coupling.

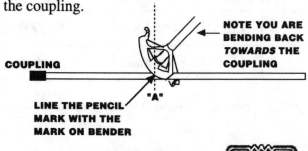

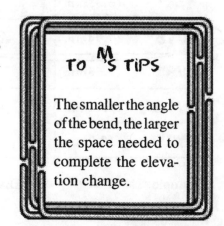

TOM'S TIPS

The smaller the angle of the bend, the larger the space needed to complete the elevation change.

TH
24

Next put the conduit handle on the floor and slide the conduit to the second pencil mark "B", rotate the conduit 180° and place mark on the **stub-up arrow**. Be careful to line up the conduit **absolutely straight** with the handle before making the second bend to avoid **dog-legging** the conduit. Bend a 30° bend.

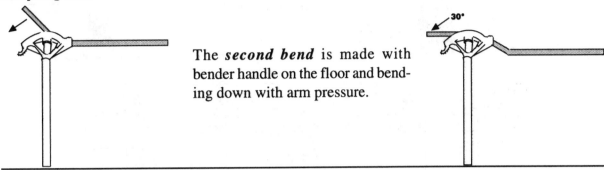

coupling end

The *second bend* is made with bender handle on the floor and bending down with arm pressure.

Sometimes a set of steps (if possible) is used to make the *second* bend. If steps or an elevated platform is not available, then invert the bender and place the handle on the floor to complete the second bend.

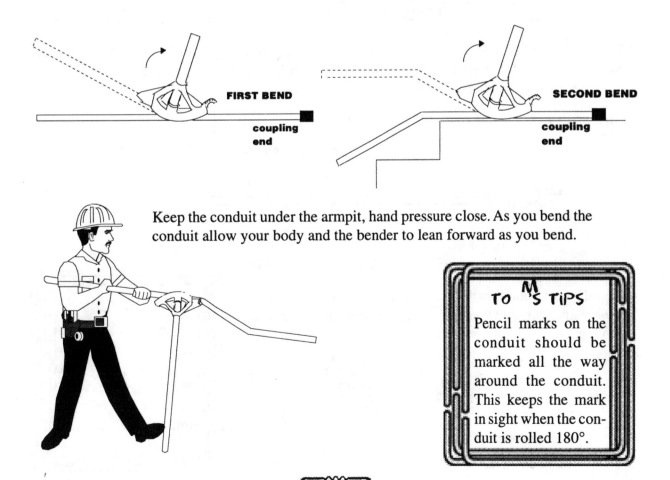

FIRST BEND

coupling end

SECOND BEND

coupling end

Keep the conduit under the armpit, hand pressure close. As you bend the conduit allow your body and the bender to lean forward as you bend.

TO**M**S TiPS
Pencil marks on the conduit should be marked all the way around the conduit. This keeps the mark in sight when the conduit is rolled 180°.

Using another 5' (1.52m) piece of 1/2" EMT the example below we have a 6" (152mm) obstruction that we need to bend a *45°* offset in the conduit to lay on top of it. Since we are working towards the obstruction we need to calculate the shrinkage in the conduit due to the detour around the 6" (152mm) obstruction. Let's say the distance from the last coupling is 24" (610mm). Now we need to add the **SHRINK AMOUNT**. The table shows for an OFFSET DEPTH of 6" (152mm) the SHRINK AMOUNT is 2 1/4" (57mm) for a 45° offset.

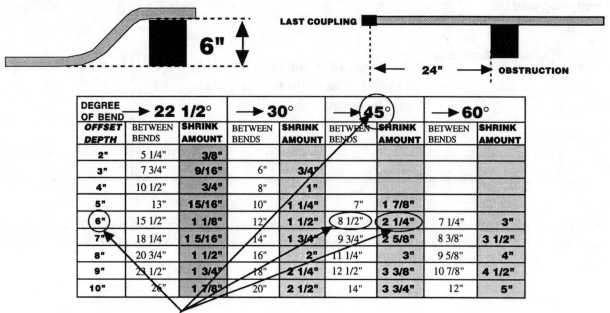

DEGREE OF BEND	→ 22 1/2°		→ 30°		→ 45°		→ 60°	
OFFSET DEPTH	BETWEEN BENDS	SHRINK AMOUNT	BETWEEN BENDS	SHRINK AMOUNT	BETWEEN BENDS	SHRINK AMOUNT	BETWEEN BENDS	SHRINK AMOUNT
2"	5 1/4"	3/8"						
3"	7 3/4"	9/16"	6"	3/4"				
4"	10 1/2"	3/4"	8"	1"				
5"	13"	15/16"	10"	1 1/4"	7"	1 7/8"		
6"	15 1/2"	1 1/8"	12"	1 1/2"	8 1/2"	2 1/4"	7 1/4"	3"
7"	18 1/4"	1 5/16"	14"	1 3/4"	9 3/4"	2 5/8"	8 3/8"	3 1/2"
8"	20 3/4"	1 1/2"	16"	2"	11 1/4"	3"	9 5/8"	4"
9"	23 1/2"	1 3/4"	18"	2 1/4"	12 1/2"	3 3/8"	10 7/8"	4 1/2"
10"	26"	1 7/8"	20"	2 1/2"	14"	3 3/4"	12"	5"

The SHRINK AMOUNT is 2 1/4" (57mm), this will add to the 24" (610mm). Make your *first* pencil mark at 26 1/4" 667mm). Your second pencil mark will be at 8 1/2" (216mm) which is the distance between 45° bends from the table.

•*Put a piece of tape on the end that is the last coupling.*

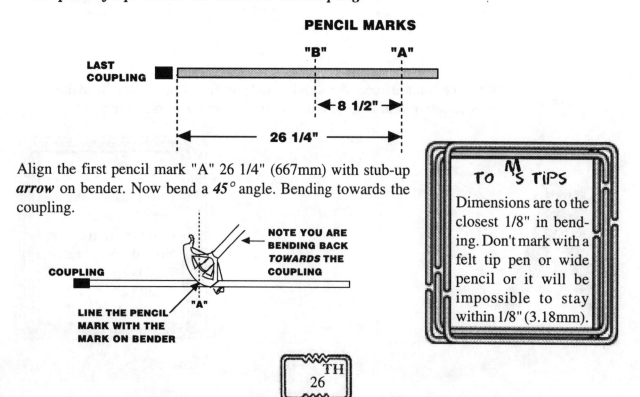

Align the first pencil mark "A" 26 1/4" (667mm) with stub-up *arrow* on bender. Now bend a *45°* angle. Bending towards the coupling.

TOM'S TIPS

Dimensions are to the closest 1/8" in bending. Don't mark with a felt tip pen or wide pencil or it will be impossible to stay within 1/8" (3.18mm).

Next lift the conduit with bender still in place and put the conduit handle on the floor and slide the conduit to the second pencil mark "B", rotate the conduit 180 and place mark on the *stub-up arrow*. Be careful to line up the conduit *absolutely straight* with the handle before making the second bend to avoid *dog-legging* the conduit. Bend a *45°* bend.

coupling end

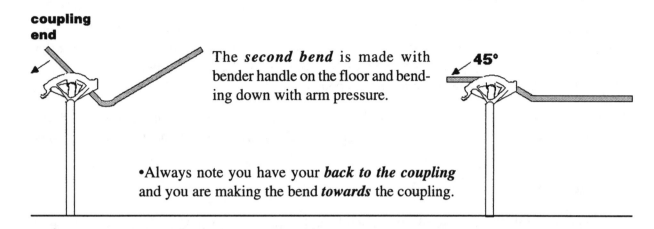

The *second bend* is made with bender handle on the floor and bending down with arm pressure.

45°

•Always note you have your *back to the coupling* and you are making the bend *towards* the coupling.

Offsets are easier to bend with the handle of the bender placed on the floor with the bender up at waist level. Bend the conduit by putting pressure on the conduit close to the bending shoe. Pull down with your hands as close to the bender head as possible to keep the radius properly formed in the bender shoe. Bending the conduit with pressure close to the bending shoe forces the conduit between the supporting walls of the shoe, which keeps the conduit from kinking and in this position it's easy to see the degree marks on the bender and accurate bends can be made.

For offsets in larger than 1 1/4" (32mm) EMT when no bender is available you can use a factory sweeping elbow and cut it in half and rotate one half and use a coupling. Greater offset depth can be obtained by using a nipple between the halves with two couplings.

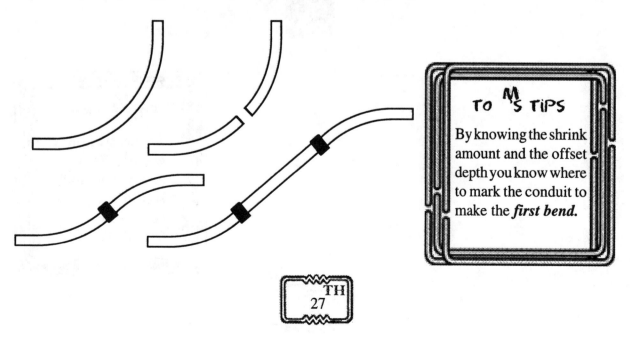

TO M'S TIPS

By knowing the shrink amount and the offset depth you know where to mark the conduit to make the *first bend.*

SADDLE BENDS

Saddles are used when something is in the way of a conduit run. There may be a beam, duct, or pipe in the path of the conduit. Bending a saddle allows the conduit to travel over or under the object and return to its original elevation.

The saddle is comprised of two offsets bent in opposite directions. The layout of a saddle is like laying out two similar offsets in opposite directions. Saddle bends should not be bent sharper than 20° to 30° if possible, since the bends are close together and if they are sharper than 30° it would make it difficult to pull the wires through the conduit.

A common fault in bending offsets or saddles is the conduit is not turned *exactly halfway* around after the first bend is made, and the reverse bend is out of line with the first one, this is called a *dog-leg*.

There are two types of saddles; a three point saddle and a four point saddle.

A three point saddle has three bends, the center bend is typically bent at 45° and the two side bends are bent at 22 1/2° each. Three point saddles should not be used for obstructions over 6 inches.

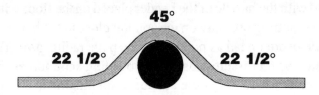

A four point saddle is really just two offsets with a measured distance between them facing each other using the same angle of degrees for each bend. Four point saddles should be used for obstructions *over 6 inches (152mm)*.

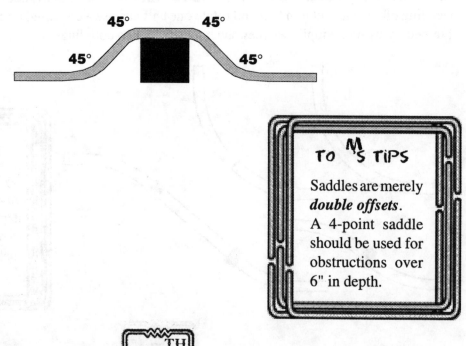

TO M S TiPS

Saddles are merely *double offsets*. A 4-point saddle should be used for obstructions over 6" in depth.

When bending a three point saddle, the **center point** of the bend must be determined first. Most benders have a mark such as a *tear drop, rim notch, "A" etc.* to indicate the center of the bend . The *rim notch, "A", or teardrop mark* is located 3/8 inches (9.53mm) closer to the hook on a 1/2" E.M.T. bender and is used rather than the star mark.

To practice, take a 10' (3.05m) length of 1/2" EMT and cut into two pieces each 5 feet (1.52m) in length. Practice bending the example with a 5' piece.

Let's bend a 3-point saddle bend to straddle a 2" (51mm) diameter obstruction using a 45° *center* bend and two *opposing* 22 1/2° bends. All measurements begin with locating the center of the obstruction and marking it as point *"A"*.

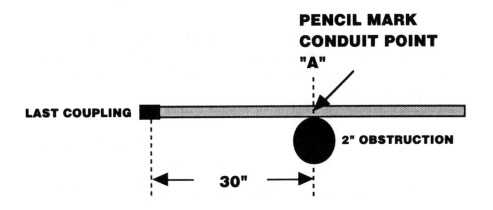

•*Put a piece of tape on the end that is the last coupling.*

Now refer to the chart below for shrinkage amount. A 2" (51mm) obstruction depth shows a shrinkage amount of 3/8" (9.53mm).

SADDLE BEND CHART FOR 45° CENTER BEND AND TWO 22 1/2° BENDS		
OBSTRUCTION DEPTH	SHRINKAGE AMOUNT MOVE CENTER MARK FORWARD	MAKE OUTSIDE MARKS FROM *NEW* CENTER MARK
1"	3/16"	2 1/2"
2"	3/8"	5"
3"	9/16"	7 1/2"
4"	3/4"	10"
5"	15/16"	12 1/2"
6"	1 1/8"	15"
FOR EACH ADDITIONAL INCH ADD	3/16"	2 1/2"

TOM'S TIPS

More skill is required in bending *offsets* compared to a 90° stub bend.

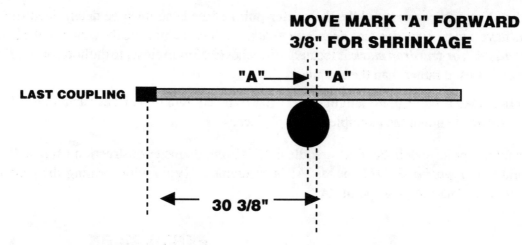

MOVE MARK "A" FORWARD 3/8" FOR SHRINKAGE

"A"→ "A"

LAST COUPLING

30 3/8"

The *new* center mark is 30 3/8" (772mm). Next we need to determine the distance between the bends from the new center mark. The chart below shows for a 2" (51mm) obstruction the distance between bends would be *5" (127mm)*. Now make two marks "B" and "C" on the conduit, each 5" (127mm) from the *new* center mark.

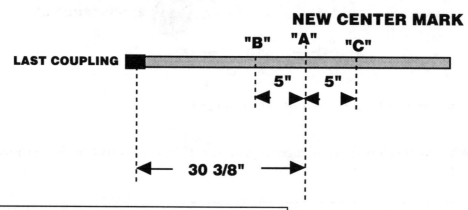

NEW CENTER MARK

"B" "A" "C"

LAST COUPLING

5" 5"

30 3/8"

SADDLE BEND CHART FOR 45° CENTER BEND AND TWO 22 1/2° BENDS		
OBSTRUCTION DEPTH	SHRINKAGE AMOUNT MOVE CENTER MARK FORWARD	MAKE OUTSIDE MARKS FROM *NEW* CENTER MARK
1"	3/16"	2 1/2"
2"	3/8"	5"
3"	9/16"	7 1/2"
4"	3/4"	10"
5"	15/16"	12 1/2"
6"	1 1/8"	15"
FOR EACH ADDITIONAL INCH ADD	3/16"	2 1/2"

•For 45° center bend and two opposing 22 1/2° bends use 3/16" per inch for shrinkage and a multiplier of 2.5 (2 1/2") for each inch of obstruction depth.

TO M⁵ TIPS

Always make the two outside pencil marks from the *new* center mark.

BENDING SEQUENCE

Step one: The first bend is *always* the 45° new center mark bend. Align mark "A" with the **RIM NOTCH** or **TEARDROP** or mark **"A"** on the bender head and bend to 45°. (•different manufacturer's have different symbols for the *center* of the bend)

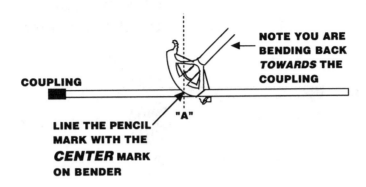

NOTE YOU ARE BENDING BACK *TOWARDS* THE COUPLING

COUPLING

LINE THE PENCIL MARK WITH THE *CENTER* MARK ON BENDER

"A"

Next put the conduit handle on the floor, rotate the conduit 180°, slide the conduit to the second pencil mark "B" and place mark on the *stub-up arrow*. Be careful to line up the conduit *absolutely straight* with the handle before making the second bend to avoid *dog-legging* the conduit. Bend a *22 1/2°* bend.

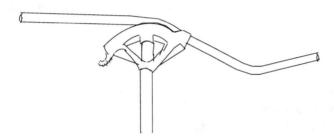

Step three: Remove and reverse the conduit and line up the last pencil mark "C" with the *stub-up arrow*. Keep the bends straight in line to avoid dog-legs. Bend to *22 1/2°*.

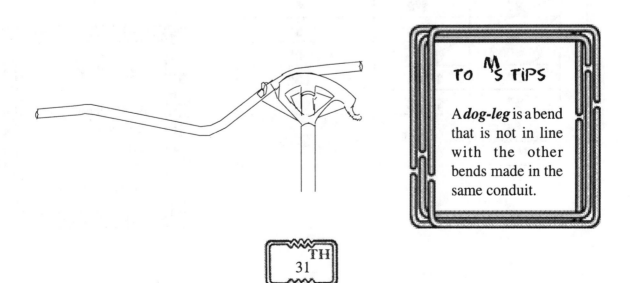

TO M S TIPS

A *dog-leg* is a bend that is not in line with the other bends made in the same conduit.

TH
31

Next let's bend a 3-point saddle bend to straddle a 4" (102mm) diameter obstruction using a 60° *center* bend and two *opposing* 30° bends. All measurements begin with locating the center of the obstruction and marking it as point *"A"*.

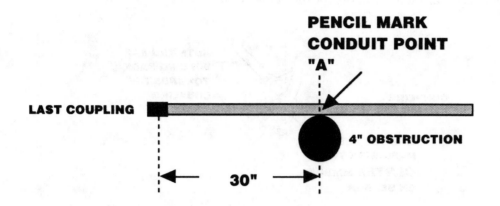

**PENCIL MARK
CONDUIT POINT
"A"**

LAST COUPLING

4" OBSTRUCTION

30"

• *Put a piece of tape on the end that is the last coupling.*

Now refer to the chart below for shrinkage amount. A 4" obstruction depth shows a shrinkage amount of 1" (25mm).

SADDLE BEND CHART FOR 60° CENTER AND TWO 30° BENDS		
OBSTRUCTION DEPTH	**SHRINKAGE AMOUNT MOVE CENTER MARK FORWARD**	**MAKE OUTSIDE MARKS FROM *NEW* CENTER MARK**
1"	1/4"	2"
2"	1/2"	4"
3"	3/4"	6"
4"	1"	8"
5"	1 1/4"	10"
6"	1 1/2"	12"
FOR EACH ADDITIONAL INCH ADD	1/4"	2"

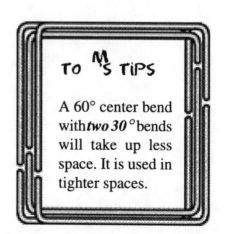

TO M S TIPS

A 60° center bend with *two 30°* bends will take up less space. It is used in tighter spaces.

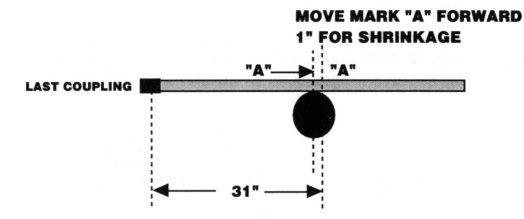

**MOVE MARK "A" FORWARD
1" FOR SHRINKAGE**

"A"   "A"

LAST COUPLING

31"

The *new* center mark is 31"(787mm). Next we need to determine the distance between the bends from the new center mark. The chart below shows for a 4" obstruction the distance between bends would be *8" (203mm)*. Now make two marks "B" and "C" on the conduit, each 8" from the *new* center mark.

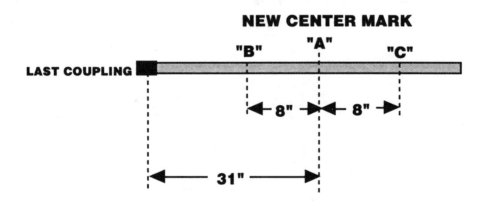

NEW CENTER MARK

"B"   "A"   "C"

LAST COUPLING

8"   8"

31"

SADDLE BEND CHART FOR 60° CENTER AND TWO 30° BENDS

OBSTRUCTION DEPTH	SHRINKAGE AMOUNT MOVE CENTER MARK FORWARD	MAKE OUTSIDE MARKS FROM *NEW* CENTER MARK
1"	1/4"	2"
2"	1/2"	4"
3"	3/4"	6"
4"	1"	8"
5"	1 1/4"	10"
6"	1 1/2"	12"
FOR EACH ADDITIONAL INCH ADD	1/4"	2"

TO M S TIPS

Care must be taken as a few degrees too much will make the offset too high. Bending less degrees will make offset too low.

BENDING SEQUENCE

Step one: The first bend is *always* the 60° new center mark bend. Align mark "A" with the **RIM NOTCH** or **TEARDROP** or mark **"A"** on the bender head and bend to 60°. (•different manufacturer's have different symbols for the *center* of the bend)

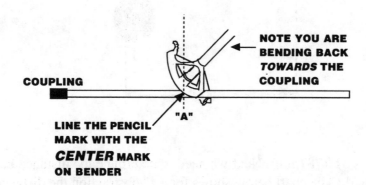

NOTE YOU ARE BENDING BACK *TOWARDS* THE COUPLING

COUPLING

"A"

LINE THE PENCIL MARK WITH THE *CENTER* MARK ON BENDER

Next put the conduit handle on the floor and slide the conduit to the second pencil mark "B" and place mark on the *stub-up arrow*. Be careful to line up the conduit *absolutely straight* with the handle before making the second bend to avoid *dog-legging* the conduit. Bend a *30°* bend.

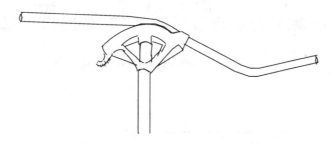

Step three: Remove and reverse the conduit and line up the last pencil mark "C" with the *stub-up arrow*. Keep the bends straight in line to avoid dog-legs. Bend to *30°*.

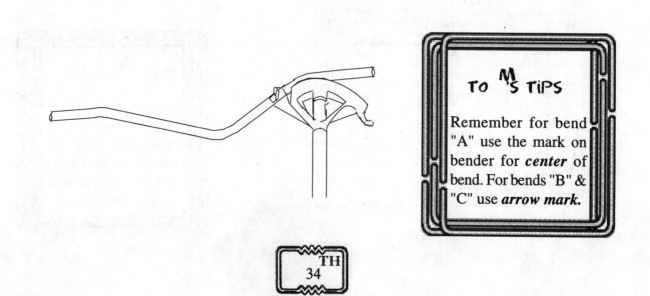

TO ^M_S TIPS

Remember for bend "A" use the mark on bender for *center* of bend. For bends "B" & "C" use *arrow mark*.

TH 34

A four point saddle is really just two offsets with a measured distance between them facing each other using the same angle of degrees for each bend. Four point saddles should be used for obstructions over 6 inches (152mm).

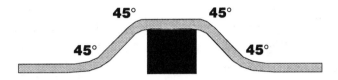

To practice, take a 10' (3.05m) length of 1/2" EMT and cut into two pieces each 5 feet (1.52m) in length. Practice bending with one 5' piece.

Let's bend a 4-point saddle over an 8" x 8" (203mm) square obstruction using four 45° bends. The obstruction is 23" (584mm) from the last conduit fitting.

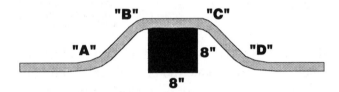

First determine the SHRINK AMOUNT. The chart below shows 3" (76mm) for an obstruction depth of 8". The 3" *adds* to the 23" for a total of 26". Mark your first pencil mark "A" at 26" (660mm).

Next determine the spacing between bends "**A**" and "**B**" both 45° bends. This will also be the distance between bends "**C**" and "**D**". The chart below shows 11 1/4" (286mm) for distance between bends.

DEGREE OF BEND →	22 1/2°		→ 30°		→ 45°		→ 60°	
OFFSET DEPTH	BETWEEN BENDS	SHRINK AMOUNT	BETWEEN BENDS	SHRINK AMOUNT	BETWEEN BENDS	SHRINK AMOUNT	BETWEEN BENDS	SHRINK AMOUNT
2"	5 1/4"	3/8"						
3"	7 3/4"	9/16"	6"	3/4"				
4"	10 1/2"	3/4"	8"	1"				
5"	13"	15/16"	10"	1 1/4"	7"	1 7/8"		
6"	15 1/2"	1 1/8"	12"	1 1/2"	8 1/2"	2 1/4"	7 1/4"	3"
7"	18 1/4"	1 5/16"	14"	1 3/4"	9 3/4"	2 5/8"	8 3/8"	3 1/2"
8"	20 3/4"	1 1/2"	16"	2"	11 1/4"	3"	9 5/8"	4"
9"	23 1/2"	1 3/4"	18"	2 1/4"	12 1/2"	3 3/8"	10 7/8"	4 1/2"
10"	26"	1 7/8"	20"	2 1/2"	14"	3 3/4"	12"	5"

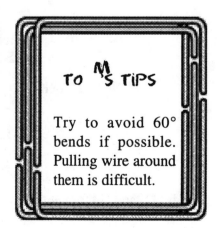

TO M'S TIPS

Try to avoid 60° bends if possible. Pulling wire around them is difficult.

Next measure from the first bend mark (pencil mark "A") 8" (203mm) across the obstruction and make a pencil mark "C". Now measure 11 1/4" (286mm) from "C" and make a pencil mark at "D".

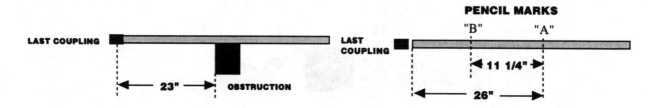

•*Put a piece of tape on the end that is the last coupling*

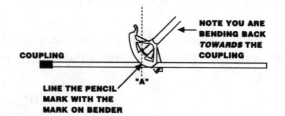

Align the first pencil mark "A" at 26" with stub-up *arrow* on bender. Now bend a 45° angle which is bend "**B**". Bending toward the coupling.

Next lift the conduit with bender still in place and put the conduit handle on the floor and slide the conduit to the second pencil mark "B", rotate the conduit 180° and place a mark on the *stub-up arrow*. Be careful to line up the conduit *absolutely straight* with the handle before making the second bend to avoid *dog-legging* the conduit. Bend a *45°* bend which is bend "**A**".

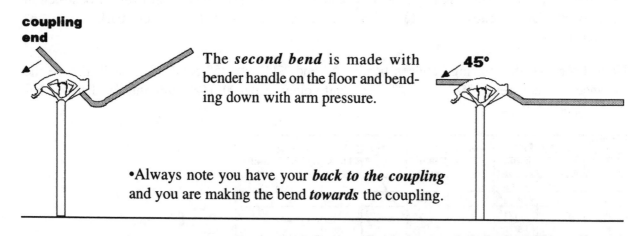

The *second bend* is made with bender handle on the floor and bending down with arm pressure.

•Always note you have your *back to the coupling* and you are making the bend *towards* the coupling.

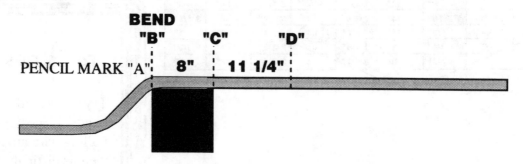

•Bends "**C**" and "**D**" are going away from the obstruction, the shrinkage amount is *not* a factor now.

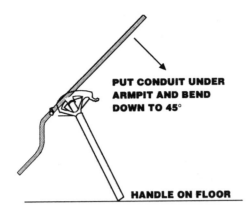

PUT CONDUIT UNDER ARMPIT AND BEND DOWN TO 45°

HANDLE ON FLOOR

Remove the conduit from the bender and reverse it in the bender, sliding the conduit down to mark "C", with handle on floor and make a 45° bend.

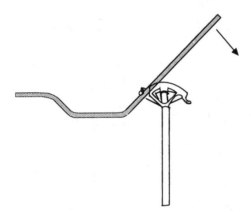

Next slide the conduit down to mark "D", rotate the conduit 180°, with handle on floor and make the final 45° bend completing the 4-point saddle.

I feel the 4-point saddle is one of the easier bends. ***The key is to start first with bend "B" which is your first pencil mark and bend towards the last coupling.***

•Note: On the video this example was made using 18" from the last fitting to the obstruction. 18" makes it a very hard bend (takes strong hand pressure). For you to practice you can use the 23" or any measurement longer. But, longer will require using a conduit longer than 5 feet in length. The choice is yours.

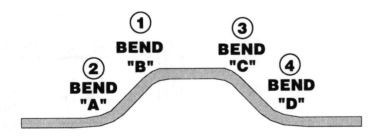

① **BEND "B"**
② **BEND "A"**
③ **BEND "C"**
④ **BEND "D"**

TO M'S TIPS

The quality of the bend depends entirely on the skill of the person bending it.

Next let's bend a 4-point saddle over an 8" x 8" (203mm) square obstruction using four *60°* bends. The obstruction is 22" (584mm) from the last conduit fitting.

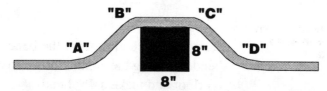

First determine the SHRINK AMOUNT. The chart below shows 4" (102mm) for an obstruction depth of 8". The 4" *adds* to the 22" for a total of 26". Mark your first pencil mark "A" at 26" (660mm).

Next determine the spacing between bends "**A**" and "**B**" both 60° bends. This will also be the distance between bends "**C**" and "**D**". The chart below shows 9 5/8" (244mm) for distance between bends.

DEGREE OF BEND	→ 22 1/2°		→ 30°		→ 45°		→ 60°	
OFFSET DEPTH	BETWEEN BENDS	SHRINK AMOUNT	BETWEEN BENDS	SHRINK AMOUNT	BETWEEN BENDS	SHRINK AMOUNT	BETWEEN BENDS	SHRINK AMOUNT
2"	5 1/4"	3/8"						
3"	7 3/4"	9/16"	6"	3/4"				
4"	10 1/2"	3/4"	8"	1"				
5"	13"	15/16"	10"	1 1/4"	7"	1 7/8"		
6"	15 1/2"	1 1/8"	12"	1 1/2"	8 1/2"	2 1/4"	7 1/4"	3"
7"	18 1/4"	1 5/16"	14"	1 3/4"	9 3/4"	2 5/8"	8 3/8"	3 1/2"
8"	20 3/4"	1 1/2"	16"	2"	11 1/4"	3"	9 5/8"	4"
9"	23 1/2"	1 3/4"	18"	2 1/4"	12 1/2"	3 3/8"	10 7/8"	4 1/2"
10"	26"	1 7/8"	20"	2 1/2"	14"	3 3/4"	12"	5"

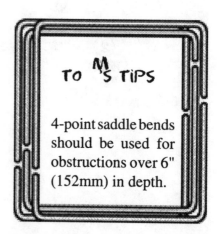

TO^MS TIPS

4-point saddle bends should be used for obstructions over 6" (152mm) in depth.

Next measure from the first bend mark (pencil mark "A") 8" across the obstruction and make a pencil mark "C". Now measure 9 5/8" from "C" and make a pencil mark at "D".

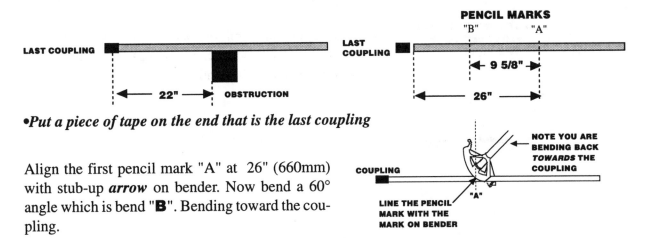

•*Put a piece of tape on the end that is the last coupling*

Align the first pencil mark "A" at 26" (660mm) with stub-up *arrow* on bender. Now bend a 60° angle which is bend "**B**". Bending toward the coupling.

Next lift the conduit with bender still in place and put the conduit handle on the floor and slide the conduit to the second pencil mark "B", rotate the conduit 180° and place a mark on the *stub-up arrow*. Be careful to line up the conduit *absolutely straight* with the handle before making the second bend to avoid *dog-legging* the conduit. Bend a *60°* bend which is bend "**A**".

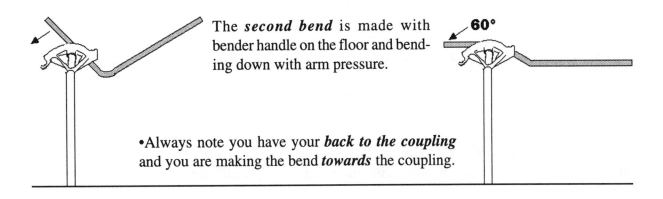

The *second bend* is made with bender handle on the floor and bending down with arm pressure.

•Always note you have your *back to the coupling* and you are making the bend *towards* the coupling.

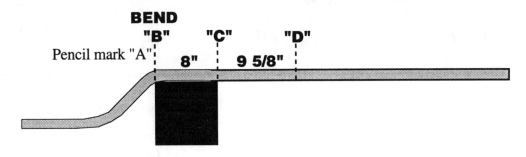

•Bends "**C**" and "**D**" are going away from the obstruction, the shrinkage amount is *not* a factor now.

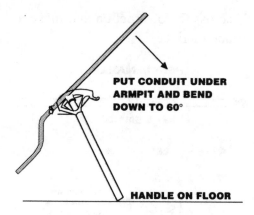

PUT CONDUIT UNDER ARMPIT AND BEND DOWN TO 60°

HANDLE ON FLOOR

Remove the conduit from the bender and reverse it in the bender, sliding the conduit down to mark "C", with handle on floor and make a 60° bend.

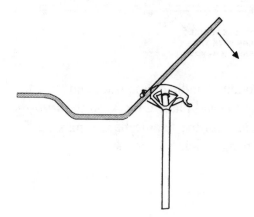

Next slide the conduit down to mark "D", rotate the conduit 180°, with handle on floor and make the final 60° bend completing the 4-point saddle.

The key is to start with bend "B" first which is your first pencil mark and bend towards the last coupling.

60° offsets are a little harder to bend as it takes more hand pressure. 60° bends should be avoided if possible as it makes wire pulling more difficult with the steeper 60° bends.

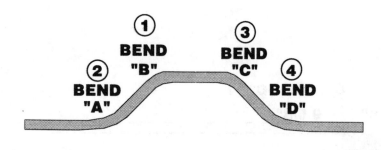

① BEND "B"
② BEND "A"
③ BEND "C"
④ BEND "D"

TO M'S TIPS

•Put a piece of tape on the end that is the last coupling, when bending this will always remind you which end is the last coupling end of conduit.

TH
40

TAKE UP AND GAIN

The arrow on the bender states for 1/2" EMT "DEDUCT 5" FOR 90° STUB". This means if you wanted a 12" (305mm) stub up you would mark the conduit at 7" (178mm) and place the arrow on the mark. The rise from the floor is composed of 7" (178mm) plus the 5" (127mm) (take-up) at the arrow for a 90° stub up of 12". Because of the sweep in the radius of the bend the actual length of conduit for this 12" stub up is 7" plus 7 5/8" (194mm) (5" + 2 5/8" gain) = *14 5/8" (371mm)*. The gain is the conduit you saved by making the bend. This gain will vary with the size of conduit used. *By knowing the gain ahead of time, you can cut and thread the conduit before bending it.*

CONDUIT TYPE AND SIZE	TAKE-UP		90° GAIN	
1/2" EMT	5"	(127mm)	2 5/8"	(67mm)
3/4" EMT or 1/2" RIGID	6"	(152mm)	3 1/4"	(83mm)
1" EMT or 3/4" RIGID	8"	(203mm)	4"	(102mm)
1 1/4" EMT or 1" RIGID	11"	(278mm)	5 5/8"	(143mm)

A curved bend requires less length of conduit than a square conduit. The difference in length is called the **gain.**

SQUARE CORNER REQUIRES MORE MATERIAL

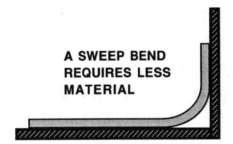

A SWEEP BEND REQUIRES LESS MATERIAL

TO M'S TiPS

Conduit systems should be installed completely before pulling any wire. Code section 300-18.

ADVANTAGES OF KNOWING THE GAIN

By knowing the *gain* you can cut and thread rigid conduit before bending it.

HOW MUCH WILL THE GAIN BE?

This depends on the size of the conduit and the radius of the bend.

CONDUIT	90° GAIN
1/2" EMT	2 5/8"
3/4" EMT or 1/2" RIGID	3 1/4"
1" EMT or 3/4" RIGID	4"
1 1/4" EMT or 1" RIGID	5 5/8"

The example is a 1/2" *rigid* conduit with the 12" (305mm) and 18" (457mm) measurements between boxes.

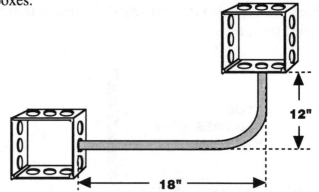

The chart above shows that 2 5/8" would be subtracted from the 12" + 18" = 30" (762mm) - 2 5/8" (67mm) for a total length of pipe of 27 3/8" (695mm).

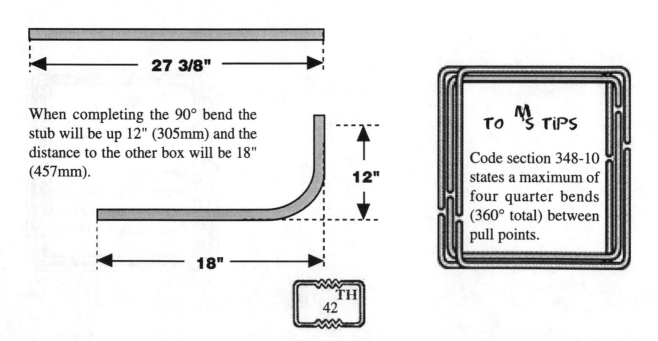

When completing the 90° bend the stub will be up 12" (305mm) and the distance to the other box will be 18" (457mm).

TO M'S TiPS

Code section 348-10 states a maximum of four quarter bends (360° total) between pull points.

TH 42

•Remember to take into consideration what type of fitting will connect the conduit to the box. It may be a box with a threaded hub, or the box shown in the example has knockouts which would require using locknuts for threaded conduit. Allowances must be made in the measuring if you are using locknuts as the threads will enter the box to accommodate the locknut or in some cases even a threaded bushing. The measurements of 12"(305mm) and 18" (457mm) in the example are to the edge of the box and do *not* include allowances for threads inside the box.

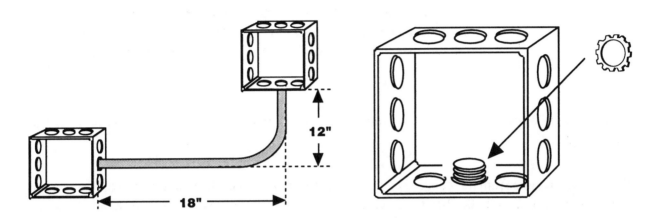

The example below shows a offset using 30° bends over a 4" (102mm) obstruction using 1/2" rigid conduit. Offsets require *more* conduit as you now are making a detour around the obstruction.

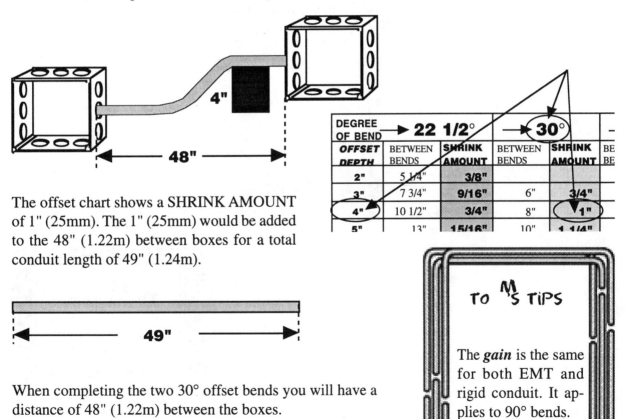

DEGREE OF BEND	→ 22 1/2°		30°		
OFFSET DEPTH	BETWEEN BENDS	**SHRINK AMOUNT**	BETWEEN BENDS	**SHRINK AMOUNT**	BE BE
2"	5 1/4"	**3/8"**			
3"	7 3/4"	**9/16"**	6"	**3/4"**	
4"	10 1/2"	**3/4"**	8"	**1"**	
5"	13"	**15/16"**	10"	**1 1/4"**	

The offset chart shows a SHRINK AMOUNT of 1" (25mm). The 1" (25mm) would be added to the 48" (1.22m) between boxes for a total conduit length of 49" (1.24m).

When completing the two 30° offset bends you will have a distance of 48" (1.22m) between the boxes.

TO M S TiPS

The *gain* is the same for both EMT and rigid conduit. It applies to 90° bends.

REBENDS OF 1/2" EMT

If you bend the conduit incorrectly the first time you may have to make a rebend.

If only the angle is wrong and nothing has damaged the wall of the conduit it is possible to straighten and rebend the conduit. For 1/2" EMT, place the handle of the bender over the stub and push down to the floor in one full sweep. You can straighten it without kinking if you're careful.

A complete 90° bend can actually be straightened with the proper technique. Don't be afraid to rebend 1/2" EMT.

Remove the handle from the bender head and slide the handle over the conduit. As you bend small segments at a time slide the handle down the conduit a little with each segment bend. Or some times it may be easier to pull the handle down in one complete motion. This you will learn as you do it.

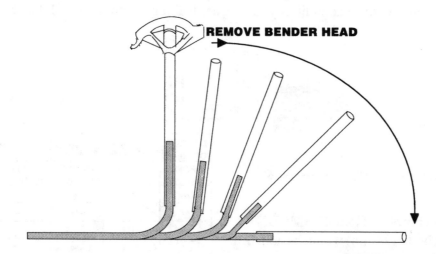

REMOVE BENDER HEAD

TO M'S TIPS

Don't use the bender head to straighten conduit. Always use the *handle* or a piece of rigid conduit.

STRAIGHTENING BENDS

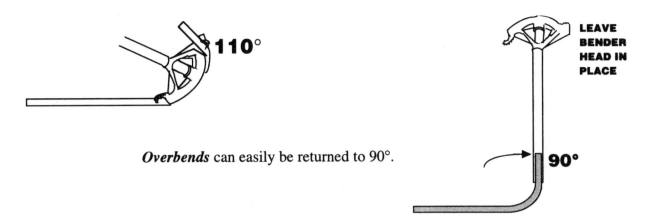

Overbends can easily be returned to 90°.

110°

LEAVE BENDER HEAD IN PLACE

90°

REMOVE THE KINKS

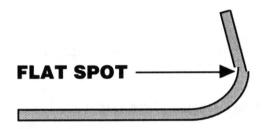

FLAT SPOT

Remove the handle from the bender head and slide the handle over the conduit. As you bend small segments at a time slide the handle down the conduit a little with each segment bend.

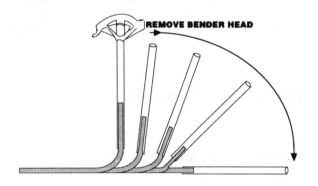

REMOVE BENDER HEAD

Next put the bender handle on the floor with the bender head in place and take the ripples out of the conduit by making small segment bends.

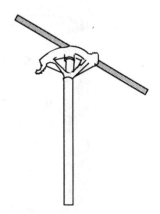

TO M S TiPS

Too many rebends will *weaken* the wall of the EMT.

TH
45

When the conduit is not turned around exactly halfway (180°) after the first bend is bent, the reverse bend is out of line with the first bend. This is commonly called a *dog-leg* by an electrician.

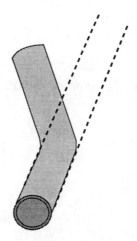

1/2" EMT can be purchased with marks painted each 1" on the conduit. This provides a straight line to follow when lining up the offset bends to avoid the dog-leg.

10' LENGTH OF 1/2" EMT WITH MARKING EACH 1"

RAISING A 90° STUB-UP

If the stub-up is too short in height, make an overbend to about 120-130°. Slide the handle down over the stub-up and pull back to 90°. This can raise a short stub-up an inch or so.

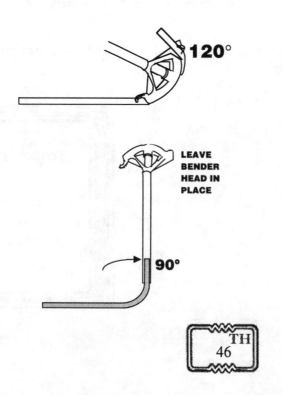

120°

LEAVE
BENDER
HEAD IN
PLACE

90°

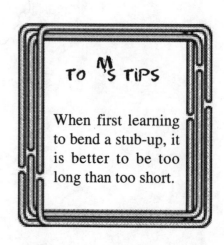

TO M'S TIPS

When first learning to bend a stub-up, it is better to be too long than too short.

TH
46

For little kicks 1" (25mm) or less into a box use 10° bends. The chart below shows a multiplier of 6 x 1" would be a distance of 6" between bends and a shrinkage of 1/16". After practice and experience small kicks can be made by eye. The larger offsets are calculated and measured.

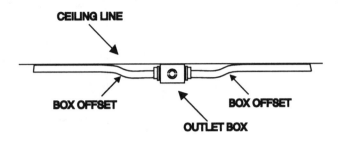

OFFSET FORMULA

Distance between bends = Depth of offset x Multiplier		
Angle	**Multiplier of Offset Depth**	**Shrinkage Per Inch**
10° x 10°	6	1/16" per inch
22 1/2° x 22 1/2°	2.6	3/16" per inch

For offsets using 22 1/2° bends the multiplier is 2.6 and the shrinkage is 3/16" per inch.

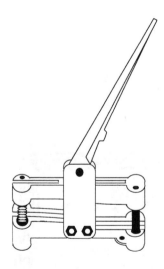

A special tool can be purchased to produce exact offsets made with 1/2" and 3/4" EMT.

TO M'S TIPS

Conduit work should look straight and square, not kinked, crooked, or creased.

When running conduit always try to keep it *flat against the wall and ceiling*.

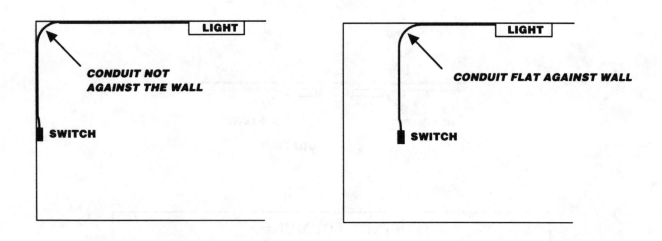

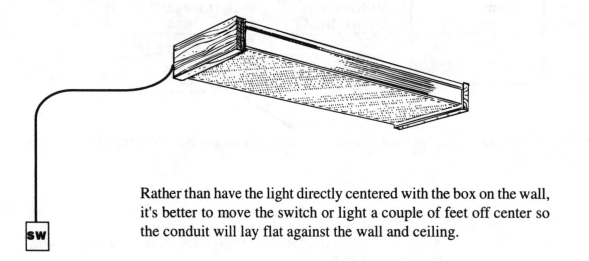

Rather than have the light directly centered with the box on the wall, it's better to move the switch or light a couple of feet off center so the conduit will lay flat against the wall and ceiling.

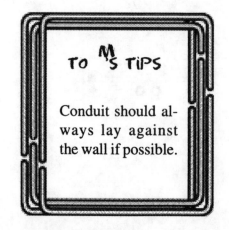

TO^MS TIPS

Conduit should always lay against the wall if possible.

Don't confuse the hickey with the roll-type hand bender. Both are used to bend conduit by hand, but in totally different ways. The roll-type bender supports the walls of the conduit and provides a bending radius that conforms to the Code requirements.

The hickey is used for rigid conduit only and the person holding the handle must form the bend as well as the radius as the bender is applied. This must be done in such a manner so as not to flatten or kink the conduit. The hickey is used somewhat like the hydraulic bender as you make segment bends. Several segment 10° bends are made to complete the bend at the proper radius. Hickeys should not be used to bend EMT because very little support is given to the walls of the conduit.

It would require nine 10° segment bends to make a 90° stub-up bend.

Effective hand bending with a hickey type bender is limited to 1/2", 3/4", and 1" rigid conduit.

TO M'S TIPS

All bends made with a *hickey* bender should be made on the floor.

A ruler has 16 marks per inch. Each mark represents 1/16th of an inch. 12 inches equal one foot.

The metric measurement uses words like millimeter (mm), centimeter (cm), and meter (m).

A millimeter (mm) is .001 meters and .03937 of an inch (between 1/32" and 3/64").

A centimeter (cm) is .01 meters and .3937 of an inch (approximately 13/32").

A meter (m) is 1 meter and 39.37 inch (approximately 39 3/8").

There would be 100 centimeters in one meter (39.37/.3937 = 100).

There would be 10 millimeters in one centimeter (.3937/.03937 = 10).

There would be .1 centimeters in one millimeter (.03937/.3937 = 0.1).

Example: 4" would have 102mm (4"/.03937 = 101.6).

Example: 12" would have 305mm (12"/.03937 = 304.8)

Example: 10' would have 3.05m (120"/39.37 = 3.048).

Example: 4" would have 10cm (4"/.3937 = 10.16).

Example: 12" would have 30.5cm (12"/.3937 = 30.48).

Example: 5' would have 1.52m (60"/39.37 = 1.524).

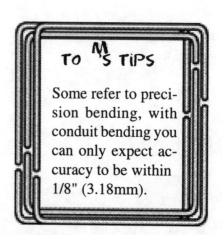

TO M'S TIPS

Some refer to precision bending, with conduit bending you can only expect accuracy to be within 1/8" (3.18mm).

DEFINITIONS

Bend - To turn or force from straight to curved or angular.

Bender - One that bends.

Curve - To have or take a turn, change, or deviation from a straight line without sharp breaks or angularity.

Circle - A ring, a closed curved line whose points are all the same distance from its center.

Circumference - The distance around the circle (external boundary).

Degree - The arc of a circle is equal to 1/360 of the circumference.

Diameter - The length of a straight line through the center of a circle.

Radius - The distance from the center point to the edge of the circle.

A circle can be divided into four equal quadrants. Each quadrant accounts for 90° and makes a total of 360°. A quarter of a circle is one quadrant (90°).

When bending a 90° stub we are in effect making a bend 1/4 of 360° or 1/4 of a circle.

1/4 of the circle

FORMULAS

C = circumference   D = diameter $\pi = 3.14$

$C = \pi D$ $C = 2\pi R$

TO M'S TIPS
Conduit runs of over 100' are not practical. Always keep in mind the *length* of your fish tape and voltage drop rules.

An attempt has been made in this program to represent the subject of conduit bending in a logical manner.

Many charts, formulas, tips, and practical suggestions have been added to give interest to the pages. Special effort has also been directed toward rendering the information given, of such practical utility that the work may serve as a trustworthy guide; to this end some simplified rules have been introduced, with plain examples of their application.

In short, the contents of the book will, it is thought, justify its name as a *workbook.*

Once on the job you'll learn new ways, different tricks, short cuts, etc. from the person who has been bending conduit for years. Soon you'll develop the method you like best.

Practice makes perfect. Now that you have started, you are on your way!

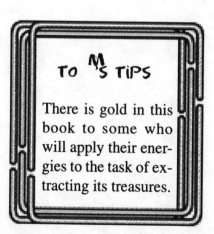

TO M S TIPS

There is gold in this book to some who will apply their energies to the task of extracting its treasures.

THE EXAM

TO M S TIPS

Sighting down the
conduit and being
careful not to turn
the conduit will
eliminate dog-legs.

TH
53

1. What is the total length of 1/2" EMT required between the boxes shown below?

$12'' + 24'' = 36''$

$36'' - 2\frac{5}{8}''_{gain} = 33\frac{3}{8}''$

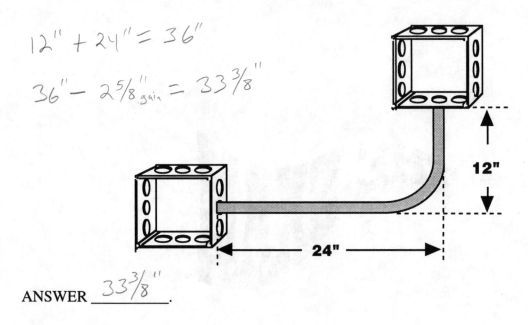

ANSWER $33\frac{3}{8}''$.

2. What is the total length of 1/2" EMT required between the boxes shown below?

$Shrink = \frac{3}{4}''$

USE 30° OFFSET BENDS

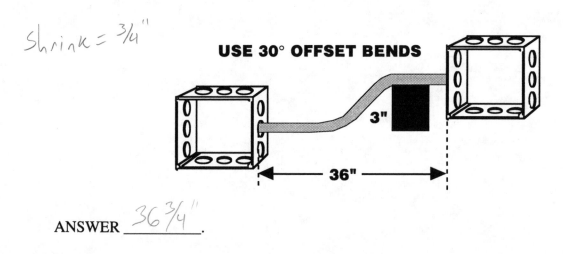

ANSWER $36\frac{3}{4}''$.

3. Four point saddle bends should be used for obstructions over _____ inches in depth.

ANSWER $6''$.

4. A measurement of 13/16" is decimal ___.

ANSWER __.8125__.

5. A measurement that reads 6 5/16" has ____ millimeters.

ANSWER __160.34__.

7.94 + (25.4 × 6)

6. The largest size roll-type hand bender for EMT is ____.

ANSWER __1¼"__.

7. The "tear drop" symbol on the bender head is the mark for a ____.

ANSWER __3 point saddle center bend__

8. What is the total length of 1/2" EMT required between the boxes shown below?

66" - (2⅝×2)

66 - 5.25

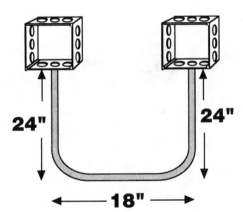

24"   24"

← 18" →

ANSWER __60.75__.
__60¾__

9. A standard conduit bend for a 3/4" conduit has a minimum radius to the center of the conduit of ____.

ANSWER __4 ½"__.

10. The suggested handle length for a 1" hand bender is ____ inches.

ANSWER __44"__.

11. The take-up for a 3/4" EMT 90° bend is ___ inches.

ANSWER ___6"___.

12. For offsets with 2" depths ____ degree bends are best.

ANSWER ___22 1/2___.

13. The distance between 45° offset bends with a 9" obstruction would be ____ inches.

ANSWER ___12 1/2"___.

14. The multiplier of offset depth for 22 1/2° bends is ____.

ANSWER ___2.6___.

15. What is the total length of 1/2" EMT required between the boxes shown below that has a 3-point saddle over a 3" obstruction?

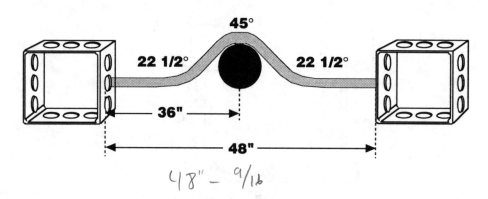

48" − 9/16

ANSWER ___47.4375___.
47 7/16

16. For a 3-point saddle bend with a 60° center bend and two 30° bends the shrinkage amount for a 5" obstruction would be ____ inches.

ANSWER ___1 1/2"___.

17. A 4-point saddle with 45° offset bends over a 7" obstruction would have a distance between bends of ____ inches.

ANSWER __9 3/4"__.

18. What is the total length of 1/2" EMT required between the boxes shown below that has a 4-point saddle over a 10" obstruction that is 12" wide?

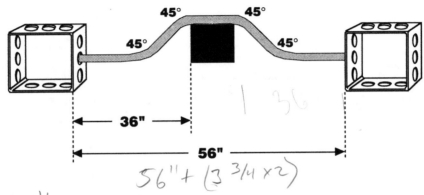

56" + (3 3/4 x 2)

ANSWER __63 1/2__.

19. The most common used angle for bending offsets in conduit to ease wire pulling is ____ degrees.

ANSWER __30°__.

20. To make a 90° 12" stub-up bend using 3/4" EMT you would place the pencil mark on the arrow symbol at ___ inches.

ANSWER __6"__.

21. The "star" symbol on the bender head is the mark for a ____.

ANSWER _Back to back bend_

22. A decimal of .625 would be ___ inches.

ANSWER ___5/8"___.

23. The shrinkage amount for a 30° offset bend over a 4" obstruction would be ____ inches.

ANSWER ___1"___.

24. For a 3-point saddle with a 45° center bend and two 22 1/2° bends over a 4" obstruction, you would make the outside pencil marks ____ inches from the new center mark.

ANSWER ___10"___.

25. For a 3-point saddle with a 60° center bend and two 30° bends over a 6" obstruction, you would make the outside pencil marks ____ inches from the new center mark.

ANSWER ___12"___.

26. The 90° gain for a 1" EMT in a stub-up bend of 12" would be ____ inches.

ANSWER ___4"___.

27. A 1/2" EMT has a ____ shrinkage per inch for a small offset of 10°.

ANSWER ___1/16___.

28. The "arrow" symbol on the bender head is the mark most commonly used for a ____.

ANSWER ___90° stub-up___

TH
58

29. What is the total length of 1/2" EMT required between the boxes shown below that has a 3-point saddle over a 2" obstruction?

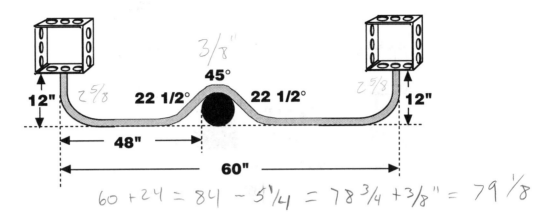

$$60 + 24 = 84 - 5\tfrac{1}{4} = 78\tfrac{3}{4} + 3/8" = 79\tfrac{1}{8}$$

ANSWER $79\tfrac{1}{8}$.

30. What is the total length of 1/2" EMT required between the boxes shown below that has a 4-point saddle over a 7" obstruction that is 10" wide?

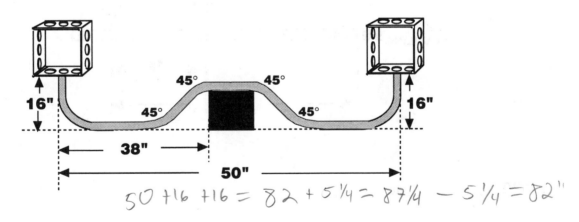

$$50 + 16 + 16 = 82 + 5\tfrac{1}{4} = 87\tfrac{1}{4} - 5\tfrac{1}{4} = 82"$$

ANSWER $82"$.

31. What is the total length of 3/4" EMT required between the boxes shown below that has 22 1/2° offset bends over a 4" obstruction?

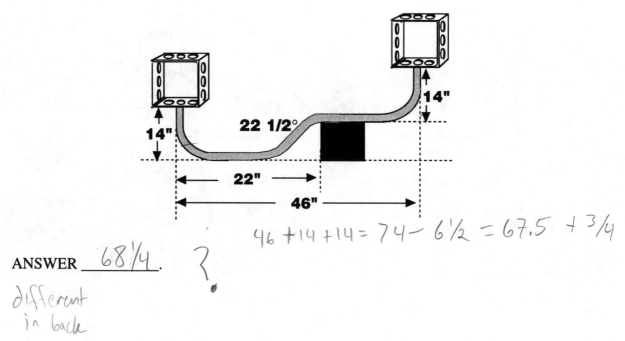

46 + 14 + 14 = 74 − 6½ = 67.5 + ¾

ANSWER _____68¼_____. ?

different
in back

32. A 6" obstruction is 41" from the last coupling. Using 3/4" EMT with 45° offsets you would put pencil mark "A" at _____ inches and pencil mark "B" at _____ inches from mark "A".

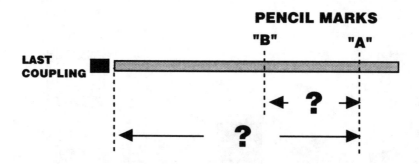

ANSWER _____43¼_____ and _____8½_____.

33. The Code allows a total of 360° in a run of conduit between boxes. Does the sketch below violate this Code rule?

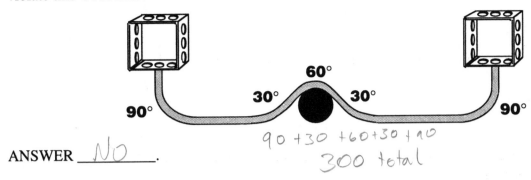

60°

30°   30°

90°   90°

90 +30 +60+30 +90

300 total

ANSWER ___No___.

34. A measurement of 17/32" would be ____ decimal and ____ millimeters.

ANSWER __.53125__ and __13.49mm__.

35. A 3-point saddle bend over a 7" obstruction using a 60° center bend and two 30° bends would have the new center pencil mark moved forward ____ inches due to the amount of shrinkage.

ANSWER __1 3/4__.

36. The take-up for a 1" EMT 90° bend is ___ inches.

ANSWER __8"__.

37. If the back to back bends are *too close together*, then reverse the bender and make a stub-up bend. Now deduct 5" (127mm) for 1/2" EMT and put your pencil mark on the ____ symbol for a stub-up bend.

ANSWER __arrow__.

38. Some refer to precision bending, with conduit bending you can only expect accuracy to be within ____ inch.

ANSWER __1/8"__.

39. Condulet fittings such as LL's, LR's, and LB's are used mostly to ____.

ANSWER _turn corners_

40. Unlike the 90° stub-up bend that is measured over-all, the offset bend is measured ____.

ANSWER _bottom to bottom_

41. The only time we need to be concerned about the *gain* of a conduit is when installing *rigid* conduit and you want to ____.

ANSWER _thread the ends first_

42. The fewer number of conduit fittings used in the raceway system the more ___ the ____ ____ will be if you're using the metal conduit as the grounding conductor.

ANSWER _effective ground path_

43. The 90° gain for a 3/4" EMT in a stub-up bend of 8" would be ____ inches.

ANSWER _3 1/4"_.

44. A standard 1/2" conduit bend has a minimum radius to center of conduit of ____ inches.

ANSWER _4"_.

45. The Code requires conduit to be securely fastened in place at least every ____ feet and within ____ feet of each box, conduit body, or other tubing termination.

ANSWER _10 , 3_

46. When bending an offset going towards an object the length of conduit will ____due to this detour and the object.

ANSWER _Shrink_

47. The distance between bends for 22 1/2° bends with a 2" obstruction would be _____ inches.

ANSWER ___5 1/4"___.

48. The total degree of bends in the conduit run shown below is _____ degrees.

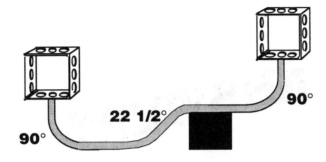

ANSWER ___225°___.

49. A 4" obstruction is 30" from the last coupling. Using 1/2" EMT with 30° offsets you would put pencil mark "A" at _____ inches and pencil mark "B" at _____ inches from mark "A".

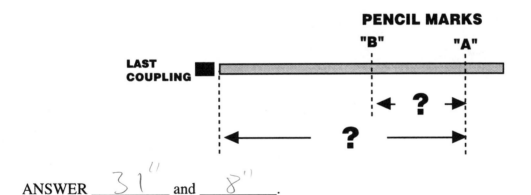

ANSWER ___31"___ and ___8"___.

50. For a 3-point saddle bend with a 45° center bend and two 22 1/2° bends the shrinkage amount for a 3" obstruction would be _____ inches.

ANSWER ___9 7/16"___.

ANSWERS

CONDUIT	90° GAIN
1/2" EMT	2 5/8"
3/4" EMT or 1/2" RIGID	3 1/4"
1" EMT or 3/4" RIGID	4"
1 1/4" EMT or 1" RIGID	5 5/8"

1. The chart shows that 2 5/8" gain would be subtracted from the 24" + 12" = 36". 36" - 2 5/8" = *33 3/8" total length.*

Page 42 Chart

•*Always remember to add the threads inside the box for total length if threaded conduit is used.*

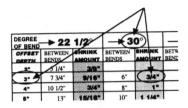

2. The chart shows a shrink amount of 3/4". The 3/4" would be added to the 36" between boxes for a total length of *36 3/4".*

Page 22 Chart

3. Four point saddle bends should be used for obstructions over *6"* in depth. **Page 28**

4. Divide 13 by 16 = *.8125.* **Page 23 Chart**

5. 6.3125/.03937 = *160mm.* **Page 50**

6. *1 1/4".* **Page 3**

7. The "tear drop" symbol is for a *3-point saddle center bend.* **Page 4**

CONDUIT	90° GAIN
1/2" EMT	2 5/8"
3/4" EMT or 1/2" RIGID	3 1/4"
1" EMT or 3/4" RIGID	4"
1 1/4" EMT or 1" RIGID	5 5/8"

8. The chart shows that 2 5/8" x 2 = 5 1/4" gain would be subtracted from the 24" + 24" + 18" = 66" - 5 1/4" = *60 3/4" total length.*

Page 42 Chart

•*Always remember to add the threads inside the box for total length if threaded conduit is used.*

9. A 3/4" conduit has a minimum radius to center of conduit of *4 1/2".* **Page 7**

10. The suggested handle length for a 1" hand bender is *44 inches.* **Page 4**

11. The take-up for a 3/4" EMT 90° bend is **6 inches**. **Page 5 Chart**

12. For offsets with 2" depths **22 1/2 degree** bends are best. **Page 16**

13. The distance between bends for 45° bends with a 9" obstruction would be **12 1/2 inches**.
Page 22 Chart

14. The multiplier of offset depth for 22 1/2° bends is **2.6**. **Page 22 Chart**

SADDLE BEND CHART FOR 45° CENTER BEND AND TWO 22 1/2° BENDS		
OBSTRUCTION DEPTH	SHRINKAGE AMOUNT MOVE CENTER MARK FORWARD	MAKE OUTSIDE MARKS FROM *NEW* CENTER MARK
1"	3/16"	2 1/2"
2"	3/8"	5"
3"	9/16"	7 1/2"
4"	3/4"	10"
5"	15/16"	12
6"	1 1/8"	1/2"15"
FOR EACH ADDITIONAL INCH ADD	3/16"	2 1/2"

15. A 3" obstruction shows a shrinkage of 9/16" from the chart. 9/16" x 2 = 1 1/8". This would add to the 48" between boxes for a total length of **49 1/8"**.

Page 29 Chart

16. For a 3-point saddle bend with a 60° center bend and two 30° bends the shrinkage amount for a 5" obstruction would be **1 1/4 inches**. **Page 32 Chart**

17. A 4-point saddle with 45° offset bends over a 7" obstruction would have a distance between bends of **9 3/4 inches**. **Page 35 Chart**

DEGREE OF BEND	22 1/2°		30°		45°		—
OFFSET DEPTH	BETWEEN BENDS	SHRINK AMOUNT	BETWEEN BENDS	SHRINK AMOUNT	BETWEEN BENDS	SHRINK AMOUNT	BET BEN
2"	5 1/4"	3/8"					
3"	7 3/4"	9/16"	6"	3/4"			
4"	10 1/2"	3/4"	8"	1"			
5"	13"	15/16"	10"	1 1/4"	7"	1 7/8"	
6"	15 1/2"	1 1/8"	12"	1 1/2"	8 1/2"	2 1/4"	7
7"	18 1/4"	1 5/16"	14"	1 3/4"	9 3/4"	2 5/8"	8
8"	20 3/4"	1 1/2"	16"	2"	11 1/4"	3"	9
9"	23 1/2"	1 3/4"	18"	2 1/4"	12 1/2"	3 3/8"	10
10"	26"	1 7/8"	20"	2 1/2"	14"	3 3/4"	BET BEN

18. A 10" obstruction shows a shrinkage of 3 3/4" from the chart. 3 3/4" x 2 = 7 1/2". This would add to the 56" between boxes for a total length of **63 1/2"**.

Page 35 Chart

19. The most common used angle for bending offsets in conduit to ease wire pulling is **30° degrees**.
Page 16 and 22

20. To make a 90° 12" stub-up bend using 3/4" EMT you would place the pencil mark on the arrow symbol at **6 inches**. **Page 5 Chart**

21. The "star" symbol on the bender head is the mark for a ***back to back bend***. **Page 4 Chart**

22. A decimal of .625 would be ***5/8 inches***. **Page 23 Chart**

23. The shrinkage amount for a 30° offset bend over a 4" obstruction would be ***1 inch***.
Page 22 Chart

24. For a 3-point saddle with a 45° center bend and two 22 1/2° bends over a 4" obstruction, you would make the outside pencil marks ***10 inches*** from the new center mark. **Page 29 Chart**

25. For a 3-point saddle with a 60° center bend and two 30° bends over a 6" obstruction, you would make the outside pencil marks ***12 inches*** from the new center mark. **Page 32 Chart**

26. The 90° gain for a 1" EMT in a stub-up bend of 12" would be ***4 inches***. **Page 42 Chart**

27. A 1/2" EMT has a ***1/16"*** shrinkage per inch for a small offset of 10°. **Page 22 Chart**

28. The "arrow" symbol on the bender head is the mark for a ***90° stub-up bend*** .
Page 4 Chart

29. A 2" obstruction shows a shrinkage of 3/8" from the chart below, 3/8" x 2 = 3/4". This would add to the 12" + 60" + 12" + 3/4" = 84 3/4". The chart below shows a gain of 2 5/8" x 2 = 5 1/4". This would subtract from the 84 3/4" - 5 1/4" = ***79 1/2" total length of conduit.***

SADDLE BEND CHART FOR 45° CENTER BEND AND TWO 22 1/2° BENDS

OBSTRUCTION DEPTH	SHRINKAGE AMOUNT MOVE CENTER MARK FORWARD	MAKE OUTSIDE MARKS FROM NEW CENTER MARK
1"	3/16"	2 1/2"
2"	3/8"	5"
3"	9/16"	7 1/2"
4"	3/4"	10"
5"	15/16"	12"
6"	1 1/8"	1/2"15"
FOR EACH ADDITIONAL INCH ADD	3/16"	2 1/2"

CONDUIT	90° GAIN
1/2" EMT	2 5/8"
3/4" EMT or 1/2" RIGID	3 1/4"
1" EMT or 3/4" RIGID	4"
1 1/4" EMT or 1" RIGID	5 5/8"

DEGREE OF BEND	22 1/2°		30°		45°	
OFFSET DEPTH	BETWEEN BENDS	SHRINK AMOUNT	BETWEEN BENDS	SHRINK AMOUNT	BETWEEN BENDS	SHRINK AMOUNT
2"	5 1/4"	3/8"				
3"	7 3/4"	9/16"	6"	3/4"		
4"	10 1/2"	3/4"	8"	1"		
5"	13"	15/16"	10"	1 1/4"	7"	1 7/8"
6"	15 1/2"	1 1/8"	12"	1 1/2"	8 1/2"	2 1/4"
7"	18 1/4"	1 5/16"	14"	1 3/4"	9 3/4"	2 5/8"
8"	20 3/4"	1 1/2"	16"	2"	11 1/4"	3"
9"	23 1/2"	1 3/4"	18"	2 1/4"	12 1/2"	3 3/8"
10"	26"	1 7/8"	20"	2 1/4"	14"	3 3/4"

Page 29 Chart   **Page 42 Chart**   **Page 22 Chart**

30. A 7" obstruction shows a shrinkage of 2 5/8" from the chart above, 2 5/8" x 2 = 5 1/4". This would add to the 16" + 50" + 16" + 5 1/4" = 87 1/4". The chart above shows a gain of 2 5/8" x 2 = 5 1/4". This would subtract from the 87 1/4" - 5 1/4" = ***82" total length of conduit.***

31. A 2" obstruction shows a shrinkage of 3/8" from the chart below for 22 1/2° offsets. This would add to the 14" + 46" + 14" + 3/8" = 74 3/8". The chart below shows a gain of 3 1/4" x 2 = 6 1/2". This would subtract from the 74 3/8" - 6 1/2" = *67 7/8" total length of conduit.*

DEGREE OF BEND	22 1/2°		BET BEN
OFFSET DEPTH	BETWEEN BENDS	SHRINK AMOUNT	
2"	5 1/4"	3/8"	
3"	7 3/4"	9/16"	
4"	10 1/2"	3/4"	
5"	13"	15/16"	
6"	15 1/2"	1 1/8"	
7"	18 1/4"	1 5/16"	
8"	20 3/4"	1 1/2"	
9"	23 1/2"	1 3/4"	
10"	26"	1 7/8"	

Page 22 Chart

CONDUIT	90° GAIN
1/2" EMT	2 5/8"
3/4" EMT or 1/2" RIGID	3 1/4"
1" EMT or 3/4" RIGID	4"
1 1/4" EMT or 1" RIGID	5 5/8"

Page 42 Chart

32. A 6" obstruction is 41" from the last coupling. Using 3/4" EMT you would put pencil mark "A" at *43 1/4"* (41" + 2 1/4") and pencil mark "B" at *8 1/2 inches* from mark "A".

DEGREE OF BEND	22 1/2°		30°		45°		60°	
OFFSET DEPTH	BETWEEN BENDS	SHRINK AMOUNT	BETWEEN BENDS	SHRINK AMOUNT	BETWEEN BENDS	SHRINK AMOUNT	BETWEEN BENDS	SHRINK AMOUNT
2"	5 1/4"	3/8"						
3"	7 3/4"	9/16"	6"	3/4"				
4"	10 1/2"	3/4"	8"	1"				
5"	13"	15/16"	10"	1 1/4"	7"	1 7/8"		
6"	15 1/2"	1 1/8"	12"	1 1/2"	8 1/2"	2 1/4"	7 1/4"	3"
7"	18 1/4"	1 5/16"	14"	1 3/4"	9 3/4"	2 5/8"	8 3/8"	3 1/2"
8"	20 3/4"	1 1/2"	16"	2"	11 1/4"	3"	9 5/8"	4"
9"	23 1/2"	1 3/4"	18"	2 1/4"	12 1/2"	3 3/8"	10 7/8"	4 1/2"
10"	26"	1 7/8"	20"	2 1/2"	14"	3 3/4"	12"	5"

Page 22 Chart

33. *NO.* The total degree of bend in the run is 90° + 30° + 60° + 30° + 90° = 300° total.

Page 42 Tom's Tips

34. A measurement of 17/32" would be 17 divided by 32 = *.53125 decimal* and .53125 divided by .03937 = *13.5 or 14 millimeters.* **Page 50**

SADDLE BEND CHART FOR 60° CENTER AND TWO 30° BENDS		
OBSTRUCTION DEPTH	SHRINKAGE AMOUNT MOVE CENTER MARK FORWARD	MAKE OUTSIDE MARKS FROM *NEW* CENTER MARK
1"	1/4"	2"
2"	1/2"	4"
3"	3/4"	6"
4"	1"	8"
5"	1 1/4"	10"
6"	1 1/2"	12"
FOR EACH ADDITIONAL INCH ADD	1/4"	2"

35. *1 3/4".* The chart shows for an obstruction of 6" a shrinkage of 1 1/2". For each additional inch add 1/4". The shrinkage amount for a 7" obstruction would be 1 3/4". **Page 32 Chart**

36. The take-up for a 1" EMT 90° bend is *8 inches.* **Page 5 Chart**

37. If the back to back bends are too close together, then reverse the bender and make a stub-up bend. Now deduct 5" (127mm) for 1/2" EMT and put your pencil mark on the *arrow* symbol for a stub-up bend. **Page 10**

38. Some refer to precision bending, with conduit bending you can only expect accuracy to be within *1/8 inch.* **Page 13 Tom's Tips**

39. Condulet fittings such as LL's, LR's, and LB's are used mostly to *turn corners.* **Page 2**

40. Unlike the 90° stub-up bend that is measured over-all, the offset bend is measured *bottom to bottom.* **Page 16**

41. The only time we need to be concerned about the gain of a conduit is when installing rigid conduit and you want to *thread it before bending.* **Page 17**

42. The fewer number of conduit fittings used in the raceway system the more *effective the grounding path* will be if you're using the metal conduit as the grounding conductor. **Page 2**

43. The 90° gain for a 3/4" EMT in a stub-up bend of 8" would be *3 1/4 inches*.
Page 42 Chart

44. A standard 1/2" conduit bend has a minimum radius to center of conduit of *4 inches.* **Page 7**

45. The Code requires conduit to be securely fastened in place at least every *10 feet* and within *3 feet* of each box, conduit body, or other tubing termination. **Page 15 Tom's Tips**

46. When bending an offset going towards an object the length of conduit will *shrink* due to this detour around the object. **Page 17**

DEGREE OF BEND	22 1/2°		
OFFSET DEPTH	BETWEEN BENDS	SHRINK AMOUNT	B
2"	5 1/4"	3/8"	
3"	7 3/4"	9/16"	

47. The distance between bends for 22 1/2° bends with a 2" obstruction would be *5 1/4 inches*. **Page 22 Chart**

48. The total degree of bends in the conduit run shown below is *225 degrees*. 90° + 22.5° + 22.5° + 90° = 225°. **Page 42 Tom's Tips**

DEGREE OF BEND	22 1/2°		30°		
OFFSET DEPTH	BETWEEN BENDS	SHRINK AMOUNT	BETWEEN BENDS	SHRINK AMOUNT	BE BE
2"	5 1/4"	3/8"			
3"	7 3/4"	9/16"	6"	3/4"	
4"	10 1/2"	3/4"	8"	1"	
5"	13"	15/16"	10"	1 1/4"	
6"	15 1/2"	1 1/8"	12"	1 1/2"	S

49. A 4" obstruction is 30" from the last coupling. Using 1/2" EMT with 30° offsets you would put pencil mark "A" at **31 inches** and pencil mark "B" at *8 inches* from mark "A". **Page 22 Chart**

SADDLE BEND CHART FOR 45° CENTER BEND AND TWO 22 1/2° BENDS

OBSTRUCTION DEPTH	SHRINKAGE AMOUNT MOVE CENTER MARK FORWARD	MAKE OUTSIDE MARKS FROM *NEW* CENTER MARK
1"	3/16"	2 1/2"
2"	3/8"	5"
3"	9/16"	7 1/2"
4"	3/4"	10"
5"	15/16"	12 1/2"
6"	1 1/8"	15"
FOR EACH ADDITIONAL INCH ADD	3/16"	2 1/2"

50. For a 3-point saddle bend with a 45° center bend and two 22 1/2° bends the shrinkage amount for a 3" obstruction would be *9/16 inches*.

Page 29 Chart

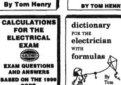

"LEARN TO BE AN ELECTRICIAN"

Starting with the toolbelt, safety, theory, practical wiring, Code, etc. Tom Henry will teach the student through his own personally designed **modules and animated videos** from point zero to an electrician that will not only know how, but *why*!

If you're a contractor that has electricians that have never had training, this will be an excellent opportunity to improve the quality and production of your work and have a person knowledgeable of the Code and able to communicate with the inspector.

This will be a correspondance course through the mail with any questions throughout the training course answered by mail, phone or fax. This training course will be offered throughout the *world*. For more information call today!

The most exciting training program ever developed! Now you'll be able to SEE the electron in orbit and SEE electricity through WATER ANALOGY in ACTION!!

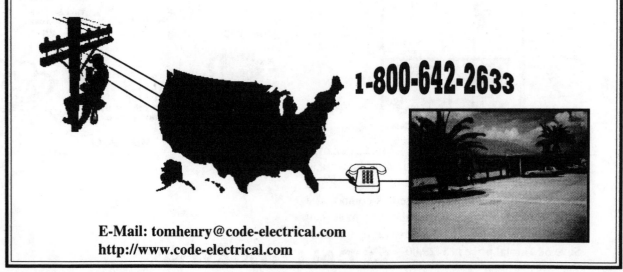

1-800-642-2633

E-Mail: tomhenry@code-electrical.com
http://www.code-electrical.com